RAMP

RISK ANALYSIS AND MANAGEMENT FOR PROJECTS

a strategic framework for managing project risk and its financial implications

Institution of Civil Engineers and The Actuarial Profession

Institution of Civil Engineers

The Actuarial Profession
making financial sense of the future

Thomas Telford

Published for The Institution of Civil Engineers and the
Faculty and Institute of Actuaries by Thomas Telford
Publishing, Thomas Telford Ltd, 1 Heron Quay,
London E14 4JD.
www.thomastelford.com

Distributors for Thomas Telford books are
USA: ASCE Press, 1801 Alexander Bell Drive, Reston, VA
20191-4400, USA.
Japan: Maruzen Co. Ltd, Book Department, 3–10
Nihonbashi 2-chome, Chuo-ku, Tokyo 103
Australia: DA Books and Journals, 648 Whitehorse Road,
Mitcham 3132, Victoria

First published 1998
Reprinted 1998
Revised, 2002
Second edition 2005

A catalogue record for this book is available from the
British Library

ISBN: 0 7277 3390 7

Designed and typeset by Kneath Associates, Swansea
Printed and bound in Great Britain by Bell & Bain, Glasgow

Foreword

Risk surrounds every human activity and influences everything we do. RAMP (risk analysis and management for projects) is a simple and straightforward process for evaluating and controlling risk in major projects, which has been developed by a joint working party of the actuarial and civil engineering professions. This handbook shows how RAMP can identify, analyse and respond to risks, and place financial values on them. Allied with sound judgement, RAMP should reduce the chance of the resources committed to a project being wasted or the project being a failure. It should also lead to better financial returns for sponsors, investors and lenders, and help to improve the consequences of projects for the wider community.

The RAMP process is concerned not only with the construction phase of a project, important though that is. It covers the entire life-cycle of the asset, with regular reviews at key points and a system for the control of those risks which remain. It can be applied both to 'hard' projects involving the construction of a physical asset and to 'soft' projects like the acquisition or disposal of a business or the launch of a new product or service.

Although RAMP was developed with major projects in mind, its principles are also applicable to smaller projects, using simplifying assumptions and less depth of analysis.

Even readers experienced in risk management can gain value from this handbook, because of the way it sets the various processes within a comprehensive framework of managerial and financial considerations, and presents a simple logical path through a complex maze. The handbook is likely to be of use to everyone who is concerned with the financial, commercial, legal or engineering aspects of projects of any kind. We are pleased to see that in 2002 a review conducted by UK Government consultants, Mott MacDonald, described RAMP as a proven method for managing project risks.

This is the second edition of the handbook and it incorporates some significant changes, with more attention being devoted to upside risks, risk efficiency, decision criteria, and the need for independent validation of appraisals. There is also some new material about public sector procurement. A new Appendix 12 presents recent evidence about the serious and sometimes unrecognised risks in major infrastructure projects, both in the UK and abroad, and makes recommendations for changes in the way these risks are approached.

Attention is particularly drawn to Appendix 7, which applies the RAMP process to a simple example. Some readers might prefer to start here before going back to the beginning.

Colin Clinton
President, Institution of Civil Engineers

Michael Pomery
President, Institute of Actuaries

Harvie Brown
President, Faculty of Actuaries

All sectors of the economy increasingly focus on the management of risk, because good risk management allows an organisation to have confidence in achieving outcomes, to constrain threat to acceptable levels and to take informed decisions about exploiting opportunities.

Governments publish guidance on the principles of risk management – HM Treasury's Orange Book, for example. However, practitioners need more than principles and RAMP brings together for those charged with delivering major infrastructure projects the combined wisdom derived from years of experience.

I commend its use to anyone embarking on a major project.

Martin Sykes,
Office of Government Commerce (UK)

Acknowledgements

This handbook has been written by a working party jointly supported by the Actuarial Profession and the Institution of Civil Engineers. The Chairman of the working party is Chris Lewin. The other members in 1998 (when the first edition of the handbook appeared) were: Professor Chris Chapman, Michael Clark, Professor Robert Clarkson, Clare Delmar, Nigel de Rivaz, Peter Hansford, Terry Mulroy, Mike Nichols, Jonathan Readings, Professor Tony Ridley, Owen Simon, Mark Symons, Luke Watts and Graham Withers.

The following are thanked for the helpful advice and assistance given to the working party: Jim Armstrong, Professor David Blockley, Mike Casebourne, Richard Chapman, Dr Sheila Farrell, Sheila Grande, John Kerman, Punit Khare, Ian Reeves, Richard Tollis, Professor Sir Frederick Warner and Brian Weavin.

The working party owes a special debt of gratitude to Mike Nichols and The Nichols Group Limited for the great contribution they made in this initiative, to Owen Simon for undertaking the considerable task of editing the first edition of the handbook and to Mark Symons for his invaluable service as Secretary of the working party.

The current (2005) members of the working party are:

Roger Allport is by profession a civil engineer and transport economist. He has spent most of his career with Halcrow, developing transport policy and major transport infrastructure projects worldwide. He is concurrently undertaking research at Imperial College into improving decision-making for major urban rail projects.

John Bennett has been responsible for a wide range of 'learned society' activities, including many externally funded research projects and special reports since joining the ICE from the oil industry in 1987. Currently he is the Chief Knowledge Manager responsible for developing knowledge products and services and enhancing their delivery through the website to members worldwide. He is secretary to the STRATrisk steering group.

Chris Chapman is Emeritus Professor of Management Science in the School of Management at the University of Southampton. He has published widely on project risk management, based on extensive experience as an international consultant. He is a Past President of the Operational Research Society, and an Honorary Fellow of the Institute of Actuaries.

Michael Clark, an actuary by profession, is the project finance manager for Sakhalin Energy, a Russian subsidiary of Shell International, where he is responsible for raising finance for the largest ever integrated oil and gas project. Prior to Shell he was involved in limited recourse and tax based funding structures at Hambros Bank. Before that, he worked for Scottish Life in Edinburgh on the development, launch and marketing of financial products.

Patrick Godfrey is a Fellow of the Royal Academy of Engineering and the Institution of Civil Engineers. He has worked throughout his career for Halcrow, providing consulting engineering services to the oil and gas, transportation and water industries. He is also the Visiting Professor of Civil Engineering Systems at the University of Bristol, an Honorary Fellow of the Institute of Actuaries and a member of the STRATrisk steering group.

Clive Hopkins is an actuary who is currently Deputy Head of Mergers & Acquisitions and Financing for Shell International. Previously he was Finance Director for Shell UK and before that Head of Group Investor Relations. He held roles in pensions management in Philips and Shell and is a former Vice Chairman of the National Association of Pension Funds.

Chris Lewin is an actuary by profession and has spent most of his career in pensions management, notably at British Rail, Associated Newspapers, Guinness and Unilever. He is chairman of the Project Risk Appraisal (RAMP) working party and a member of the STRATrisk steering group.

Mike Nichols, Chairman and Chief Executive of the Nichols Group, has a degree in economics, is a Fellow of the Institution of Civil Engineers and an Honorary Fellow of the Institute of Actuaries. He proposed the concept for RAMP and has played a major role both in its development and that of STRATrisk.

Gerald Orman worked for engineering and construction companies in the UK and overseas in major projects including mining, irrigation systems, metal industries and railways. Since forming his own risk analysis company he has advised government procurement industries, banks and insurance underwriters on project overrun risks and specific organisations such as

the Norwegian Olympic Committee on the staging of the Winter Olympics.

Jonathan Readings works for Impact Plus as a strategic change and programme management consultant serving mainly central government departments and agencies. He has more than 28 years' experience in large-scale programme management and change management programmes. Before moving into project and management consultancy he worked for 16 years as a project manager on large-scale North Sea oil projects.

Mark Symons, a barrister, was involved in insolvency administration before spending 16 years with trade associations. Since 1994 he has been at The Actuarial Profession, where he is Finance & Investment Board Practice Manager and secretary to the Project Risk Appraisal (RAMP) working party.

David Tilston is Head of Group Finance at Mowlem plc. He has held senior financial roles at Balfour Beatty, AMEC and WS Atkins as well as being Finance Director of two listed companies. He was formerly a Council Member and Chairman of the Education Committee of The Association of Corporate Treasurers.

Luke Watts, having studied risk management at Southampton University, worked in a number of risk-focused roles in professional services organisations before joining Norwich Union Insurance as a Risk Manager. In his current role he facilitates the management and communication of business risks within the organisation. Luke is an associate member of the Institution of Mechanical Engineers.

Contents

1 Introduction and summary

1.1 Introduction

This handbook describes a process for analysing and responding to risks which can affect the overall success of projects. The process is called RAMP - standing for 'risk analysis and management for projects.' It has been devised by a joint working party of the Institution of Civil Engineers and the Actuarial Profession.

In 1994 the two professions decided to establish the joint working party, consisting of experienced actuaries, civil engineers and economists, to develop a better way of looking at project risk and controlling it effectively. Both professions found that they had fundamentally the same very practical approach to risk, although sometimes using different terminologies to describe the basic concepts. By pooling their skills, knowledge and experience, derived from applying well-established techniques in widely different circumstances, they were then able to produce a risk analysis and management process which went beyond the risk management methodologies in common use by any one of the professions represented on the working party.

The handbook presents the RAMP process and acts as a guide to its use. Flowcharts and brief notes on techniques which can be applied are set out in the Appendices. This chapter starts with the rationale and context for RAMP and is followed by an overview of the RAMP process (Chapter 2), which includes an outline of the basic concepts and principles of risk. The RAMP system is explained in detail in Chapters 3 to 8. Some applications and case studies are discussed in Chapter 9 and opportunities for future development of RAMP in Chapter 10. There is a glossary and bibliography.

The twelve Appendices to the handbook provide in-depth guidance to some of the key concepts and methodologies which underpin the RAMP system, including the meaning of risk (Appendix 1) and ways to model investment (Appendix 2). Appendix 7 applies the RAMP process to a simple example. The main steps in the RAMP process are summarised in Appendices 9 and 10 for ease of reference.

Some readers may prefer to start with a case study and they should turn straight to Appendix 7.

RAMP is designed to meet a perceived need for a more rigorous approach to risk management which can be applied to all types and stages of investments - e.g. investments in new infrastructure, manufacturing plants, property developments, telecommunications networks, computer systems and new products and services. RAMP provides a method to enable a structured and consistent analysis of risk within projects (and between them) to be carried out effectively. It can be applied either at a strategic level or as a detailed analytical and control process. It assesses just how risky a potential project is, and assists in the choice of which options for designing the project should be selected.

1.2 A summary of RAMP

RAMP is a comprehensive and systematic process for identifying, evaluating and managing risks in capital investment projects. It covers the entire life of a project from inception to close-down, not just the construction stage. RAMP consists of four activities.

Activity A:	Launching the RAMP process
Activity B:	Reviewing the risks
Activity C:	Managing the risks
Activity D:	Closing down the RAMP process

The first activity is launching the RAMP process. An individual specialist or, if the investment is large, a team is appointed to implement the RAMP process. The 'baseline' objectives, scope and plans for the project are defined, as well as the underlying assumptions on which these are based.

The next activity is carrying out a risk review, which is repeated at key stages or decision points throughout the life of the investment. This involves systematically identifying risks and entering them in a risk register. Next the risks are evaluated to determine their likelihood and impact, and any relationships between them. Where appropriate, response measures are identified to avoid, reduce or transfer risks and increase the likelihood of favourable outcomes. These measures are incorporated in a risk response strategy. For those risks which remain, an investment model is used to estimate the overall riskiness and viability of the project. Assuming the project is not aborted, a risk response plan is then prepared.

The third activity, managing the risks, is conducted between risk reviews as part of the mainstream management of each stage in the life of the investment. This involves implementing the risk response strategy and risk response plan developed during the preceding risk review. Activities and events during the progress of the project are monitored to identify new or changing risks. Then appropriate measures are taken to deal with them. Designated individuals, called risk custodians, are charged with managing the risks which fall within their areas of responsibility.

The last activity is the closing down of the RAMP process, when a retrospective review is made of the investment in terms of its success in meeting its objectives, and the effectiveness of RAMP in contributing to the outcome.

1.3 Importance of risk

All projects or business ventures involve risks of various kinds. This applies to the smallest domestic project, such as the construction of a garden shed, as much as it applies to very big projects costing many millions or billions of pounds like new toll bridges, undersea links, mass transit railways, motorways and airports. In recent times there have been many examples of major projects which have either been abandoned before becoming operational, cost up to twice the budgeted amount to construct, opened twelve months late, performed well below the specified level of reliability or generated less than 50% of the forecast annual revenue. As a consequence, governments, funders and lenders have become extremely reluctant to accept the risks inherent in such investments. Some of these failures would perhaps have occurred even if a robust risk management process had been adopted, but the risks which led to failure were often foreseeable and could easily have been mitigated. The scope for projects to go disastrously wrong does not vary with their size: a simple project like the construction of a garden shed can provide just as much risk as a project many times bigger, even though the consequences of the failure of such a project might be trivial compared with the catastrophic costs associated with the failure of a major project, such as the sinking of the *Titanic* in 1912 which tragically caused the deaths of over 1600 people. Many of these deaths could probably have been avoided had the ship carried more lifeboats, at relatively insignificant extra cost. A comprehensive risk management process, such as RAMP, would have enabled the costs and benefits of installing more lifeboats to have been weighed up objectively at the outset, without being unduly influenced by the inadequate statutory requirements or the common but incorrect assumption that the ship was unsinkable.

Some readers may be surprised that the *Titanic* is described as a 'project' at the time it sank, even though it had by then entered the operating phase. The reason is that we use the word 'project' to encompass the whole investment life-cycle of an activity, not just the construction phase. In the case of a ship, the project commences when the idea of building the ship is first conceived and ends when the ship is no longer in operation and disposed of. We also apply the word 'project' to any organised business activity where an investment is made, whether it involves the creation of a physical asset or not. There may also be some surprise that the word 'failure' is used to describe the sinking of the *Titanic*. In the civil engineering profession 'failure' normally means a structural failure of the physical asset, leading to its being damaged or even destroyed. However, we are looking here at investments in terms of their overall lifetime performance, measured against the original objectives (as modified from time to time). If these objectives are not achieved, the project as a whole will usually have failed – even though the physical asset may still be intact. It is this emphasis on the whole investment life-cycle, and on the overall picture rather than the physical asset alone, which is one of the main characteristics of RAMP.

In practice, it is virtually impossible to avoid all downside risks. They can often be reduced and can sometimes be transferred – e.g. through contracts, financial agreements, concessions, franchises and insurance policies – but there is usually some residual risk. For example, the prime contractor or concessionaire can become insolvent and consequently not fulfil its obligations.

There is a growing realisation that the key to success in investments is not to ignore or be intimidated by risk, but to analyse and manage it effectively. Organisations should not necessarily be risk averse, except for risks which could threaten their survival or expose people to the possibility of serious injury or death. 'Nothing ventured, nothing

gained', as the old saying goes. One of the major advantages of risk analysis and control is that it allows profitable opportunities to be exploited, which would otherwise be judged too risky. Another advantage is that it leads to positive action to minimise the risks of adverse events as far as is practicable and economic. Risk is often most efficiently managed by arranging for it to be carried by the party best able to understand and control each risk at the lowest cost.

More attention is now being paid to upside risk – i.e. the potential for the project to have outcomes which are more favourable than expected. It is becoming recognised that steps can often be taken at the outset, as part of the risk response programme, to increase the chances of these favourable outcomes occurring and maximise the return if they do occur.

1.4 Weaknesses of existing approaches

There are a number of shortcomings in some of the current methods of dealing with project risk, including:

- weaknesses in forecasting and appraisal, arising from poor methodology or other causes
- insufficient attention to sources of possible bias in the risk assessment or project appraisal
- inadequate follow through from the analysis stage to the control of risks once the project starts to be implemented
- a concentration on risks in asset creation rather than on the potentially higher risks in other stages of the investment life-cycle (especially the operating stage)
- a tendency to focus on risks which can be most easily quantified, without the exercise of proper judgement to get a good feel for the other risks involved
- too little attention to changing risk exposures during the investment life-cycle

- no satisfactory method for combining risks – especially where, as often is the case, the separate risks are interdependent
- a lack of consistency in analysing and dealing with risks for different projects
- failure to give sufficient attention to upside risks.

As a consequence

- some types of project have a systematic pattern of failure – see Appendix 12 for examples of this
- projects are not consistently analysed, even for the same sponsoring organisation, and different standards of analysis are applied
- sponsors, investors and other interested parties cannot rely on the results of risk analysis
- downside risks which were identified for mitigation can remain unmitigated
- opportunities for improving the chances of particularly favourable outcomes may be missed
- no satisfactory framework exists for developing a record of experience concerning specific categories of risk and the associated outcomes
- there is no reliable basis for auditing risk analysis and management
- research and expertise is largely fragmented and dispersed instead of contributing cumulatively to improve the state of the art.

RAMP aims to overcome the above weaknesses.

1.5 The need for RAMP

A survey by the Confederation of British Industry (CBI) in 1994 showed that only about one-quarter of manufacturing companies used quantitative methods to assess project risk, with the majority relying on subjective judgement. There was evidence that some companies were using a very high minimum acceptable rate of return (i.e. 'hurdle rate') to judge the acceptability of projects, in the hope that this would provide a built-in contingency margin to cover risk. They probably did not realise the dangers in doing this. While it is appropriate to use a higher hurdle rate for projects having a particularly high degree of downside risk which is incapable of specific analysis and mitigation (for example, the risks associated with investment in a developing country with an unstable political regime), it is entirely inappropriate to do so for the majority of risks, which are not only capable of analysis as described here but are also often capable of mitigation. A failure to carry out proper risk analysis will often lead to some of the possibilities of risk response (for both upside and downside risks) being left unexplored. Another danger of blindly using too high a hurdle rate without proper risk analysis is that it could easily lead to the incorrect acceptance of high risk projects which may have large returns in some circumstances and the incorrect rejection of low risk projects with good returns but which fail to meet the artificially high hurdle rate.

Later surveys have confirmed the 1994 findings. Although reductions in interest rates have led to the use of somewhat lower hurdle rates, the features described above still remain.

Appendix 12 highlights some of the serious deficiencies in existing forecasting methods for major infrastructure projects, based on the available evidence, and suggests some of the steps which need to be taken to achieve improved forecasting in the future.

It seems likely that increasing attention will be paid to the appraisal and discussion of capital projects, both at their outset and once they are in operation. Rigorous analysis of the resource implications and the benefits and adverse consequences will include a review of the wider considerations such as pollution, use of scarce resources, disruption for third parties, safety, social benefit, etc. In particular it will become increasingly unacceptable to waste the world's scarce resources on projects which turn out to be a failure because the risks were inadequately appraised at the outset.

With increased dependence on advanced technology and complex infrastructure systems, the assessments of large new projects will inevitably become a more complicated process than when less advanced facilities could be built on 'greenfield' sites. Not only will the physical constraints and technological challenges become more demanding but there will be the need to take account of a much wider range of vested interests and often some powerful voices which are opposed to the project. There will be a greater range of risks to be considered and the quantification of the risks will become even more difficult. The RAMP process will help to ensure that all the additional work necessary to meet these new challenges is undertaken in the optimum manner.

One possible explanation for the use by some organisations of inadequate risk management methodologies may lie in the cultural characteristics of these organisations (see Chapter 12 of Chapman and Ward, 2002, for a review of 'cultural conditions' which can cause problems). To maximise its potential the organisation may need to change its culture. The UK Government is an example of a large organisation which is seeking to do just that. Since 2003, it has been undertaking the difficult task of introducing a risk management culture throughout central government departments. This is requiring thousands of civil servants to come to terms with new approaches and techniques, and to understand the real benefits which can be obtained from a methodical, thoughtful and well-documented approach to risk.

1.6 Special features of RAMP

The particular characteristics of RAMP include the following:

- It is a logical process, designed to provide a useful and practical framework for identifying, analysing, responding to and controlling the risks inherent in a complex activity.

- It *must* be supplemented by good judgement and common sense throughout: these are crucially important inputs. RAMP provides a framework within which sound judgements can potentially be made but it does not explain how they can be made and it certainly should never be used as a substitute for them.

- It is not just concerned with the risk of capital cost over-run. On the contrary it is designed to evaluate all major risks over the life-cycle of a project, including the vital revenue risk – i.e. the risk that the net revenue stream from a project may vary significantly from that which has been forecast.

- It studies upside risks as well as downside risks.

- It is disciplined and needs to be applied carefully, with a proper follow-through from one stage to another, so that all the major issues get addressed.

- It can be viewed as an outline route map, which will be filled out with project specific detail, in order to become useful to a variety of parties (who may each look at it from a different perspective).

- It pays special attention to disaster scenarios, even if the probability of occurrence is thought to be low.

- It recognises the critical importance of forecasting, and the need to validate forecasts.

- It links with investment models which place suitable financial values on the assessed risks, and highlights the key risk areas which must be kept under review in future.

- It shows the *order* in which the various stages of the appraisal process should be carried out, so as to keep unnecessary work to a minimum.

- It ensures that there is a strong linkage between the initial risk assessment process and the process for controlling the risks in practice once the project has reached the implementation phase.

To underline the need to apply RAMP with good judgement and common sense, it must be understood that it is not a comprehensive guide to every aspect of project appraisal. If it is used to provide a numerical result mechanically, without thought, then the process will have been misused. It can never provide reliable results if the data used as input is unreliable – 'garbage in, garbage out' applies to RAMP just as much as it does to other models. It is particularly important to ensure that the forecast cash flows for capital costs, revenues, and operating costs, etc. are as accurate and unbiased as practicable, with validation based on the evidence of past experience with similar projects, and independent checking of the figures. RAMP is not about 'box ticking' – the forms which are suggested for recording the results of the RAMP methodology impose a certain amount of discipline and structure on the process, and would be required if RAMP were to become a suite of computer programs; however, the forms are *not* the key parts of the process, although record keeping in one way or another is very important. The key part of the RAMP process, without which it will certainly fail, is an inquiring, contemplative, sceptical human mind.

1.7 Why sponsored by civil engineers and actuaries?

As designers and project managers – and in many other roles – civil engineers have a significant involvement in major projects. At the root of their professional training is the application of engineering methodologies to forces and materials to create complex structural entities like bridges, large buildings, dams, power stations, and transport infrastructure. Awareness of risk is inherently incorporated into the discipline of civil engineering, because the consequences of the failure of an engineering structure can potentially be catastrophic in terms of loss of life alone (as with the failure of a major dam). Until recently, however, civil engineers had only a limited exposure to some non-engineering financial risks – for example, inflation or the cost of capital – which are capable of having a major effect on the viability of projects. The RAMP methodology is encouraging civil engineers to become more aware of the business side of projects and the way that a wider variety of risks can be managed.

Actuaries, on the other hand, are well versed in assessing a wide range of both technical and commercial risks, in evaluating investment portfolios and in the management of insurance companies and pension funds. They can place a financial value on risks of all kinds. In a totally different way, they are as aware as civil engineers of the need for effective identification and management of risks within their core disciplines, because most investors and investing institutions are for sound logical reasons risk averse (in the final analysis, aversion is the preferred attitude of most people towards downside risk). Actuaries can assist in the introduction of RAMP into an organisation, as well as in the application of RAMP to specific projects. They are familiar with the more complex techniques which can be used. These include the calculation of a probability distribution of NPVs (net present values), using scenario analysis or stochastic modelling, to assist decision makers.

1.8 Who should use RAMP?

Although engineers and actuaries do have a strong interest in risk assessment and management, several other professions also have a legitimate involvement in the same field – notably, project managers, economists, management consultants, accountants, bankers, lawyers, fund managers, corporate finance professionals and public administrators. In fact, it is expected that RAMP will be of interest to anyone engaged in capital projects – whether as investors, decision-makers, consultants or managers.

The need for a comprehensive and systematic approach to risk management, such as RAMP, is highlighted by the increasing trend towards a broader packaging of risks – e.g. in finance-design-build-operate-maintain (FDBOM) concessions – and the transfer or sharing of risk for capital investments between public and private sectors under Public-Private Partnership schemes or the UK Government's private finance initiative. These require an assessment at an early stage of all the risks throughout the investment life-cycle from initiation, during design and construction, through the operating period, to close-down of the investment. Furthermore, the parties involved often have difficulty in understanding risks outside their area of experience and may therefore overestimate them and not wish to undertake them – e.g. contractors may be reluctant to take on operating franchises. RAMP can make a significant contribution to the analysis, allocation and management of risks for such arrangements.

1.9 What benefits does it offer?

To summarise, RAMP will:
* assist in reducing risk exposures through better information and more effective management action
* lead to better decisions and give greater confidence to investors and other stakeholders
* highlight the roles of engineers and actuaries in risk analysis and management issues generally
* provide a valuable contribution to the wider community of professionals and managers engaged in projects
* enable better use to be made of the world's scarce resources by helping to prevent waste arising from failed projects.

1.10 PRAM

In 2004 the Association for Project Management published the second edition of its guide known as PRAM (Project Risk Analysis and Management). It 'aims to assist project managers and risk practitioners by describing a range of approaches and techniques that are being used by their peers'.

We believe that the PRAM approach is basically consistent with the RAMP methodology. One of the key strengths of the PRAM guide is that it clearly describes a number of specialist techniques for risk identification, analysis and management, and shows how to put them into practice. There is also a useful chapter on behavioural issues. The guide is therefore warmly recommended reading for project managers and other experts, and rather less space is devoted here to these specialist topics than might otherwise have been the case.

In this handbook describing RAMP methodology, we have concentrated more on the *strategic* aspects of risk appraisal and management, with particular reference to the financial implications. It is vitally important that the major risks involved in a project are properly evaluated and well understood by sponsors, lenders and investors as a basis for their decisions. We consider that the use of RAMP methodology will enable the risks to be minimised and any significant remaining risks to be properly identified, quantified and controlled, in the manner that these parties need.

The handbook shows with illustrative case studies how this methodology can be applied in order to optimise decision making at the strategic level.

1.11 Internet access

RAMP has its own website: www.RAMPrisk.com

1.12 STRATrisk

As mentioned above, RAMP is a tool for the strategic appraisal of projects. The RAMP working party is now turning its attention to the wider aspects of strategic risk in existing businesses. A simple framework (currently known as STRATrisk) is emerging, which will assist company boards and public-sector decision makers to focus on the vital strategic risks and uncertainties (both upside and downside) inherent in their business activities. RAMP itself will then be viewed as an important tool within the overall framework.

2 Overview of RAMP

2.1 Basic concepts

The basic idea behind RAMP is extremely simple. It can be illustrated by considering the steps you take when planning a country walk with your family whilst on holiday. First you and your family agree the objectives for the walk. You *identify* the risks, such as being caught in a thunderstorm, encountering a muddy path or getting lost. There may also be upside risks, such as finding an excellent tearoom. You then *analyse* the likelihood of each such event and how serious the consequences might be, for example ruined clothing or getting back too late for the show you had planned to see.

The next step is to identify the *risk response options*, such as carrying umbrellas and rainwear, wearing boots, taking a map and compass, or taking a mobile phone to call a taxi if necessary. In each case there will be an inconvenience or cost factor and a decision will have to be made on whether response is worthwhile.

Unless all the risks are fully responded to, some *residual risks* will remain. Suppose you decided not to take rainwear. The residual storm risk will then have to be controlled by keeping an eye on the sky and heading for shelter in time if black clouds roll up. The time risk will likewise have to be *controlled* by occasionally looking at a watch so that the taxi can be called when necessary. If we take the mobile phone, this will introduce a *secondary* risk, namely that it might be lost or stolen.

These concepts of setting the project objective, followed by identifying, analysing and responding to the risks, and controlling the residual risks, lie at the heart of the RAMP process. For a major project the situation is much more complicated than a country walk, with far more risks and the probable introduction of numerous secondary risks arising from the response actions selected. Some of the risks will be dependent on others and many of the probabilities, costs and outcomes will be uncertain.

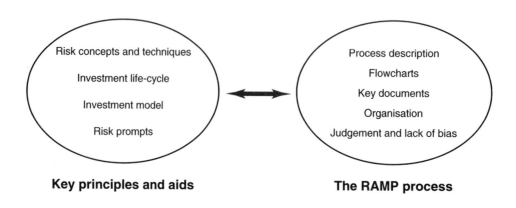

Figure 1. Components of the RAMP approach

2.2 Pre-requisites for RAMP

In order to understand and apply the RAMP approach the user needs a basic understanding of the following (see Fig.1).

- *Key principles and aids* covering some underlying concepts and techniques for risk analysis; a definition of the stages through which an investment progresses from start to finish; an investment model which relates the various costs and benefits arising from the investment to some overall measure of its value (e.g. its net present value); and risk prompts (such as checklists or risk matrices) to assist in the identification and evaluation of risks.

- *RAMP process* comprising a description of the process; supporting flowcharts; details of the key documents created during each activity of the process; and the organisation to be adopted in order to apply RAMP with good judgement in an unbiased way.

Each component is outlined in turn below, starting with those on the left hand side of Fig. 1 (the key principles and aids), followed by those on the right hand side (the components of the RAMP process).

2.3 Risk concepts and techniques

For the purpose of RAMP, 'risk' can be defined as a threat (or opportunity) which could affect adversely (or favourably) achievement of the objectives of an investment. However, users of RAMP need to have an understanding of risk which extends beyond this simple, succinct definition. They need an appreciation of some basic concepts of risk and techniques for risk analysis. These are summarised in Appendix 1. It may be useful by way of introduction to set out a few of the main ideas about risk which are applied in the RAMP process..

Overall risk

Although individual risks will be examined, the RAMP process always aims to set them eventually in the context of the combined effect of all individual risks and sources of uncertainty – i.e. *the overall risk.*

Risk events

In any risk analysis, it is necessary to begin by identifying the *risk events*, which, if they occurred, could affect the outcome of the project, for better or worse (e.g. the collapse of a tunnel during construction of an underground railway). Particular attention should be paid to the identification of those events which could have very serious adverse implications for the project, even if they seem unlikely to happen (such as the sinking of the *Titanic*).

It is also important to think hard about whether there are some possible outcomes, which could normally not be foreseen, because they depend on an unusual combination of circumstances or a change in the underlying situation which has not been envisaged. An example is the possibility that new warships might have to be sold to other navies, instead of being brought into commission as intended. The consideration of such risks (as far as this may be possible) is very important indeed; simply because they are unknown, such risks are very easy to omit. One of the crucial tasks in the RAMP process is to strive to identify as many of these risks as possible, despite the undoubted difficulties, since experience shows that it is such risks which are often the most dangerous for the viability of a project.

Likelihood

The next step is to assess the *likelihood* of each risk event occurring; this means the chance (or 'risk') that it will occur. Thus a 20% likelihood means that there is a one in five chance that the risk event will happen. It is twice as likely to occur as it would be if there was only a 10% likelihood. An event which is unlikely to happen has a likelihood only slightly greater than zero, whereas an event which is almost certain to happen has a likelihood only slightly less than 100%. In effect, therefore, we have a continuous scale of measurement, ranging from 0% to 100%, to express the degree of likelihood that an event will happen.

Another way of looking at likelihood, which some readers may find helpful, is to imagine the project being repeated (if that were possible) a very large number of times. Then an event with a likelihood of 10% could be expected to occur in about 10% of the projects and an event with a likelihood of 20% in about 20% of the projects.

Often the occurrence or non-occurrence of a particular risk event will depend on the occurrence or non-occurrence of a number of underlying causes. It is often more appropriate to concentrate the analysis of likelihood on underlying causes, rather than the risk event itself. For example, suppose the event under consideration is that of a bridge collapsing during construction. Two possible independent underlying causes of such a collapse might be identified – e.g. a design fault (having, say, a 0.05% likelihood) or faulty assembly (having, say, a 0.10% likelihood). Although we can add the two probabilities together (as they are small and independent of each other) and say that the chance of the bridge collapsing is assessed as about 0.15%, we must record the two underlying causes separately in order to facilitate the study of risk mitigation options at a later stage of the analysis.

We have spoken as if we know for certain that a particular risk event has a fixed numerical chance of occurring. In practice, it is usually not known with absolute precision what the chance of occurrence actually is. All we have is a perception, based on opinion and research, which is probably not quite correct and may occasionally be wide of the mark. For example, the true chance of occurrence of an

event which is assessed as having a likelihood of 20% might be, say, 25%, although we may never get to know the latter figure (see the section 'Uncertainty' in Appendix 1). For this reason the sensitivity of calculations must be tested by varying the values assumed, to see whether this makes much difference to the picture which emerges from the analysis.

This concept of sensitivity testing is of great importance in risk analysis. Whenever an assumption is made or a value is estimated, the effect of using credible alternative assumptions or values must be evaluated and recorded. The results thus obtained will be useful in assessing the reliability of the overall analysis and may sometimes point to a greater range (or a more dispersed probability distribution) of possible outcomes for the project as a whole than is otherwise indicated.

Sometimes, of course, we may be well aware that we do not have nearly enough information to assess the likelihood with even a tolerable degree of accuracy. In other words, there is a high degree of uncertainty. We might know enough to be able to say that the likelihood probably lies within certain specified limits, but if this is a wide band for an event which would have significant consequences if it occurred, the result might well be that we are unable to make rational decisions about the future of the project. In such a situation it might be worth carrying out research to improve our knowledge and reduce the uncertainty. Suppose, for example, that the initial assessment is that an event which could have very serious adverse consequences has a likelihood which could be anywhere in the range of 0% to 25%. If the risk could not be eliminated, transferred or avoided, it is unlikely that the sponsor would proceed with the project. If, however, research was undertaken which showed that the true likelihood was around 1%, many sponsors would be prepared to accept this comparatively low risk and go ahead. Uncertainty is often more difficult to analyse and 'manage' than risk, although the downside possibilities associated with uncertainty can often be mitigated to some extent, despite the lack of accurate knowledge.

Impact

Up to this point we have been concerned only with the chance or likelihood that a particular event occurs. However, we also need to consider the possible consequences if it occurs – e.g. a delay, and in particular the financial consequences, which we call the *impact*. Clearly, it is important to do this, since a 5% likelihood of losing £1 million is much more serious than a 5% likelihood of losing only £1000. Sensitivity testing is important here too.

Expected value

We can obtain a good measure of the financial value or cost to be placed on different downside risks by multiplying the likelihood by the impact, to give the *expected value*. Thus a 5% likelihood of losing £1 million would have an expected value of £50 000. A 5% likelihood of losing £1000 would have an expected value of £50.

One way of looking at the expected value is that it is equivalent to the insurance premium which one would have to pay an insurance company in order to cover the risk (ignoring the loadings which the insurance company would apply in practice for expenses, profit, etc.). Thus the premium would have to be £50 000 to cover a 5% risk of losing £1 million. This is because if there were a large number of such risks being covered by the insurance company, the total of the premiums would then approximately equal the sums paid out in claims for the events which occur. The expected value is therefore a good measure of the true financial value of the risk, taking into account both the likelihood that the event will occur and the impact if it does.

Often, however, an event (if it occurs) will not have a single unique impact. There may be a range of possible impacts, each with a different probability. In such cases it may be appropriate to derive the expected value of the risk by using the average impact, obtained by weighting each of the possible impacts by its own probability. In some circumstances even a small adverse event could have a serious or even catastrophic effect on a complex integrated system, and this possibility needs very careful consideration, even for risks which might appear at first sight to give rise to trivial consequences. As in the old adage, 'For want of a nail the kingdom was lost'. If such dangers exist for the project being analysed, sufficient attention must be given to the risks concerned and ways of responding to them.

Risk efficiency

The RAMP process requires a systematic search to find responses to some of the individual risks, to achieve risk efficiency. This occurs when a set of responses is found beyond which the marginal cost of introducing an additional response would exceed the utility to the sponsor of the resulting downside risk reduction or opportunity increase. A reasonably aggressive approach is taken towards assuming risk in order to increase the expected reward, provided that the sponsor's risk tolerance is not exceeded.

Prioritising risks

The concepts *overall risk, risk events, likelihood, impact, expected value* and *risk efficiency* lie right at the heart of RAMP. They enable us to place a realistic financial value on each risk, depending on how likely the event in question is to occur and what would be the impact if it did. We can then rank them in order of importance and we can also form a preliminary idea of how much it is worth spending in order to mitigate them. For example, it would not normally be worth spending £20 000 in order to mitigate a non-catastrophic risk which has an expected value of only £1000.

However, it would be dangerous if decision-makers were to look only at expected values when deciding on whether to proceed with a project. This is because expected values conceal some of the more extreme possible outcomes. For example, if there is a chance of 0.1% that an event will occur costing £10 million, the expected value of this risk will be only £10 000. If one were only considering expected values, this risk would seem less important than another risk having an expected value of £30 000, based on a 40% likelihood of an event having an impact of £75 000. Nevertheless, the occurrence of the first of the two risk events mentioned above could cripple or bankrupt the sponsor. Hence the sponsor will often wish to pay particular attention to the existence of such a risk and seek to mitigate it as far as possible, even if the cost of doing so exceeds the expected value.

Probability distribution

It is important to show decision-makers the full range of possible financial outcomes for the project as a whole (taking account of all the risks to which it is subject) and the degree of likelihood which can be attached to each outcome. This is called a *probability distribution* of possible outcomes, and is another key concept of RAMP. It is a measure of the overall risk in the project. The decision-maker will use it as a basis for deciding whether the degree of downside risk is acceptable or not. In doing so he or she will exercise judgement, bearing in mind the extent to which the sponsor could afford to bear the more unfavourable outcomes, should they occur, and the likelihood that such outcomes will happen. The decision-maker will also take into account the possible upside outcomes and their likelihood.

Using judgement

The risk analyst must be able to think very clearly in order to distinguish between the various types of risk, combine them correctly with due allowance for mutual dependency where relevant, and avoid falling into the many traps which exist for the unwary. It is not a matter of carrying out mechanical analysis, but of keeping a clear head and a questioning frame of mind. Risk specialists are trained and experienced in such work, and it will usually be worthwhile to employ them from the outset (possibly using an external consultancy firm), to avoid unwise decisions or disappointments when lenders or investors refuse to proceed because the risks are too high.

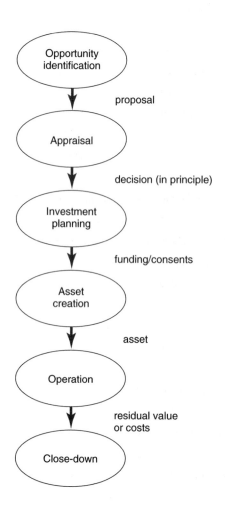

Figure 2. Investment life-cycle

Risk of bias

A key strategic risk, which needs very careful consideration, is that the whole of the risk analysis and investment appraisal of a project may be biased, either by accident or design:

- Insufficient care may have been devoted to the identification or analysis of risks.
- Key risks may have been accidentally or deliberately omitted.
- Incorrect assumptions that certain risks are independent of each other may have concealed the true likelihood of 'chain reactions' of adverse events.
- The likelihood of disasters occurring may have been underestimated because of inadequate past experience.
- Cash flows may have been guessed or, worse, deliberately biased towards optimism.
- Insufficient account may have been taken of the future ups and downs of the economic cycle.
- The risks associated with new technologies may have been given inadequate attention.
- Not all the effects of the project on the sponsor's other business may have been considered.
- Credit may have been taken for benefits not directly attributable to the project.
- The assumptions on which the estimates are based may not correspond with senior management's view of the world in future.
- Arithmetic or spreadsheets may contain errors which lead to substantially incorrect evaluation, or there may be failures of logic.

These, and similar issues, could well invalidate the whole risk management and investment appraisal exercise. There is strong evidence – see Appendix 12 – that some of these problems may well have existed in many big projects in the recent past. The key step which should be taken to reduce this strategic risk is to validate the work (and in

particular the estimated cash flows) by competent and genuinely independent checking, and by reference where possible to the outcomes of similar projects undertaken previously. Senior management should pay particular attention to the main assumptions which have been made and to possible sources of bias, including any failure on their own part to provide adequate resources for the project, the appraisal or the risk management process.

2.4 Investment life-cycle

The investment life-cycle is a description of the successive stages through which an investment progresses from start to finish. It defines the overall framework within which RAMP is carried out. The version of the investment life-cycle adopted for RAMP has six separate but sometimes overlapping stages as described below.

- *Opportunity identification:* in which the potential investment is identified, and an initial assessment is made to decide whether to proceed with a full appraisal.
- *Appraisal:* which involves determining the investment objectives, scope and requirements; defining the project structure and strategy; developing the business case; identifying funding options; identifying, analysing and deciding how to respond to the risks; and conducting a feasibility study prior to deciding whether to make the investment.
- *Investment planning:* comprising the procurement of funding; obtaining of planning consents; undertaking preliminary design work; planning project implementation; preparing a detailed risk response plan; and making a final decision to proceed with the investment.
- *Asset creation:* including planning, designing, procuring, constructing and commissioning the asset. (This stage is sometimes referred to as 'the project' but in this handbook we use the

Table 1. Activities, key parameters and RAMP process in each stage of investment life-cycle

Investment stage/ Objective	Principal activities	Key parameters	RAMP process
Opportunity identification To identify opportunity and decide whether it is worthwhile conducting a full appraisal	Identify business need Define investment opportunity Make initial assessment Decide whether to proceed with appraisal	Broad estimate of capital cost and cash flows Cost appraisal	Preliminary review
Appraisal To decide whether the investment should be made	Define investment objectives, scope and requirements Define project structure and strategy Develop business case Identify funding options Conduct feasibility study Decide (in principle) whether to proceed with investment	Refined estimates of capital cost and cash flows Cost of investment planning phase	Full risk review
Investment planning To prepare for effective implementation of the project	Procure funding Obtain planning consents Preliminary design work Compile project implementation plan Place advance contracts (e.g. site preparation) Make final decision to proceed with investment	Financing cost Refined estimates of capital cost and cash flows	Risk review (prior to final decision)
Asset creation To design, construct and commission the asset, and prepare for operation	Mobilise the project team Detailed planning and design Procurement/tendering Construction Testing, commissioning and hand-over Ensure safety Prepare for operation	Project objectives: - scope* - performance/quality* - timing* - capital cost	Risk reviews (during or towards end of each activity) and risk management between risk reviews
Operation To operate the asset to obtain optimum benefits for sponsor and other principal stakeholders (including investors and customers)	Operate the service Derive revenue and other benefits Maintain and renew the asset	Operating cost Maintenance cost Cost of renewals Revenue Non-revenue benefits	Risk reviews (periodically)
Close-down To complete investment, dispose of asset and related business, and review its success	Sale, transfer, decommissioning or termination of asset and related business Post-investment review	Decommissioning cost Cost of staff redundancies Disposal cost Resale or residual value	Final risk review and RAMP close-down

* These have a potential impact on one or more financial parameters word 'project' to mean the activities occurring during the whole life-cycle of the investment.)

- *Operation:* using the asset to provide a service so as to derive revenue and other benefits, while maintaining and renewing the asset.
- *Close-down:* which refers to the end of the investment life-cycle, when the franchise or concession period ends, or when the asset is sold or reaches the end of its economic life and is decommissioned.

The six stages of the investment life-cycle, and the main end results from each stage, are shown in Fig. 2. The above stages may, of course, be varied in practice to meet the requirements of a particular situation.

The RAMP approach aims to identify, evaluate and manage the risks, which could cause the project to vary from the most likely or expected outcome. Table 1 shows the main objectives, activities, associated

parameters and risk management processes in each stage of the investment life-cycle.

Three key management roles need to be performed in carrying out the successive stages of a capital investment: the sponsor, project manager and operator. The sponsor is, or acts for, the project owner and is therefore accountable for the overall investment. The project manager is accountable to the sponsor for the planning and execution of the work to create the asset needed to achieve the objectives of the investment. The operator is responsible for using the asset to provide the benefits expected from the investment. Although the sponsor has overall responsibility, all three roles need to be involved at various stages of the investment life-cycle.

The sponsor is most directly and actively concerned in the first three stages, which involve defining, developing and justifying the investment and obtaining funding and planning consents. Typically, a development manager will be delegated responsibility

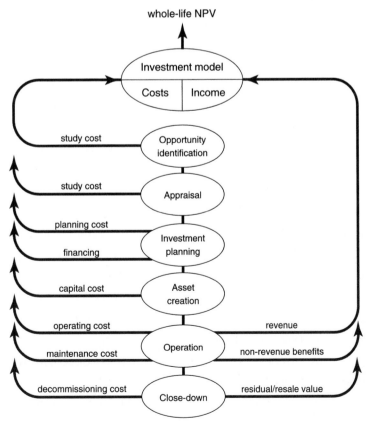

Figure 3. Investment model

for managing these early stages. The project manager directs the fourth stage to create the asset. The operator has primary responsibility for operating the asset and generating benefits (in the fifth stage). All three roles may be involved in the sixth and final stage, close-down, the leading role depending on the situation and nature of close-down.

2.5 Investment model

A way is needed for evaluating financially the risks to which an investment is exposed in terms of the objectives and the parameters used to define them (e.g. revenue, other benefits, capital and operating costs). Also needed is some overall measure of the value of the investment (e.g. pay-back, IRR (internal rate of return) or whole-life NPV). A suitable investment model needs to be developed in order to

- estimate the likely financial outcome of the project and ascertain whether it meets any predetermined financial criteria as to what constitutes a viable project
- estimate the extent to which the financial outcome may vary from the likely value, and the probabilities of different degrees of variation
- show which methods of risk response are financially worthwhile.

An appropriate structure for such a model is illustrated in Fig. 3. Details of how the model can be constructed and used in conjunction with RAMP are set out in Appendix 2. The key parameters are gross revenues, the value of any other benefits, capital costs and operating costs.

For preliminary appraisals a simple investment model can often be processed by hand with the aid of no more than a pocket calculator. For a full appraisal it would be more typical for the investment model to be set out in the form of a spreadsheet, which is processed by computer. Where, as is often the case for major projects, the

main aim of the investment model is to calculate the NPV of the project, each parameter in the financial model is represented by a single value or a series of cash flows. Each of these is then converted into an NPV using an appropriate discount rate, so that the estimated whole-life NPV for the project can be calculated. During the RAMP process, the financial model is used repeatedly to assess how potential impacts of risks on the individual parameters affect the whole-life NPV of the investment – i.e. the 'riskiness' of the investment. This is typically done by using scenario analyses, Monte Carlo simulation or sensitivity analysis. A similar method can be used to compute the IRR where this is required.

2.6 Risk prompts

One of the main tasks in RAMP is to identify risks as comprehensively as possible. A risk which has not even been identified cannot be analysed or evaluated, and no response to it can be formulated. Hence, it is of great importance to do everything possible to list every risk to which the project in question could be exposed. Brainstorming sessions and desk studies are very useful for this purpose but in addition it is often helpful to use risk prompts, which suggest possible areas of risk, to uncover further risks which may affect the project. Examples of risk prompts are checklists, risk maps and risk matrices. Appendix 3 sets out an example of a comprehensive risk matrix and Appendix 1 (page 87) gives a checklist of unexpected risks. Appendix 7 (page 106) lists some risks that are commonly found in projects. Appendix 12 reports on some of the risks in major infrastructure projects.

2.7 Process description

The RAMP process consists of four *activities*, which are generally carried out at different times in the

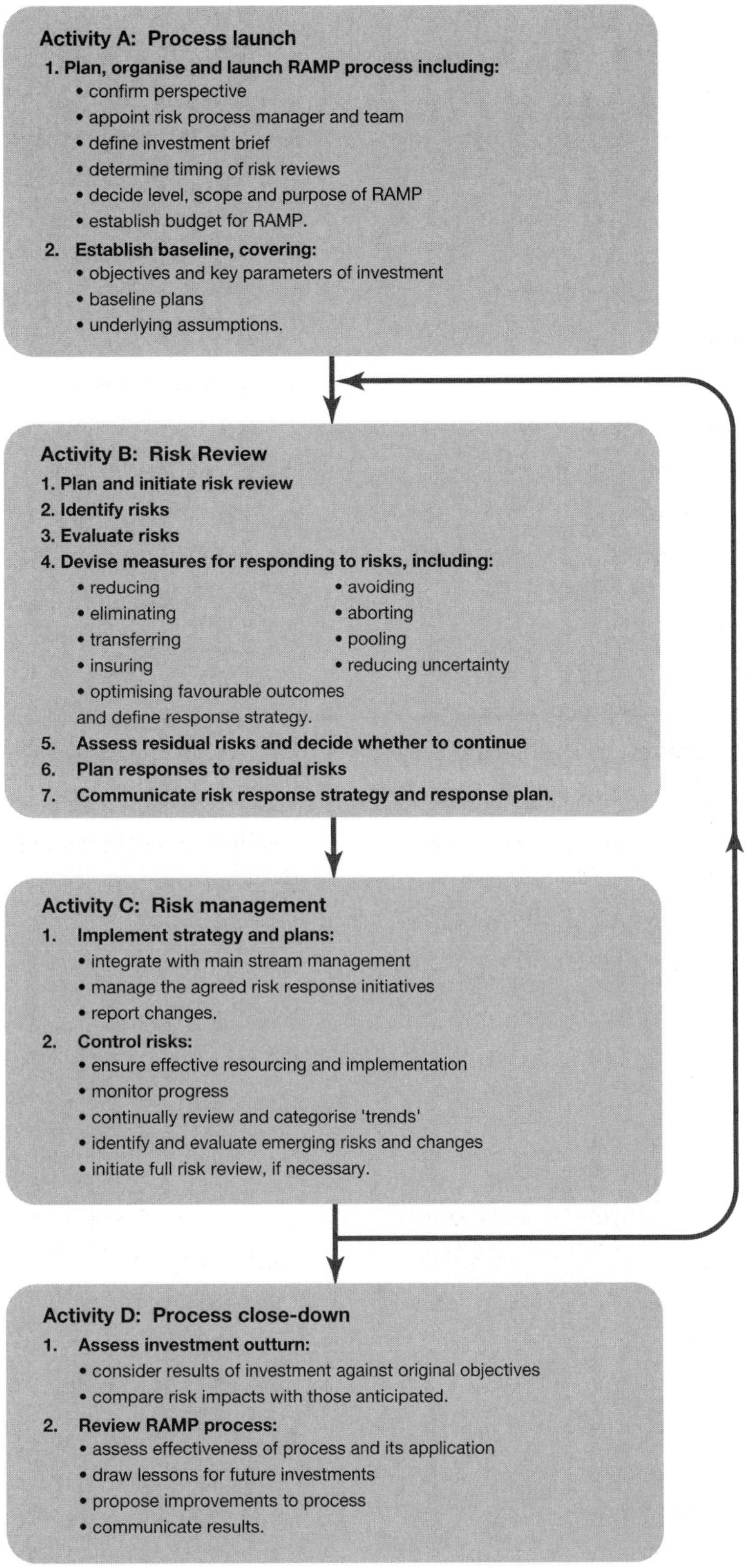

Activity A: Process launch

1. **Plan, organise and launch RAMP process including:**
   - confirm perspective
   - appoint risk process manager and team
   - define investment brief
   - determine timing of risk reviews
   - decide level, scope and purpose of RAMP
   - establish budget for RAMP.
2. **Establish baseline, covering:**
   - objectives and key parameters of investment
   - baseline plans
   - underlying assumptions.

Activity B: Risk Review

1. **Plan and initiate risk review**
2. **Identify risks**
3. **Evaluate risks**
4. **Devise measures for responding to risks, including:**
   - reducing
   - eliminating
   - transferring
   - insuring
   - optimising favourable outcomes
   - avoiding
   - aborting
   - pooling
   - reducing uncertainty

   and define response strategy.
5. **Assess residual risks and decide whether to continue**
6. **Plan responses to residual risks**
7. **Communicate risk response strategy and response plan.**

Activity C: Risk management

1. **Implement strategy and plans:**
   - integrate with main stream management
   - manage the agreed risk response initiatives
   - report changes.
2. **Control risks:**
   - ensure effective resourcing and implementation
   - monitor progress
   - continually review and categorise 'trends'
   - identify and evaluate emerging risks and changes
   - initiate full risk review, if necessary.

Activity D: Process close-down

1. **Assess investment outturn:**
   - consider results of investment against original objectives
   - compare risk impacts with those anticipated.
2. **Review RAMP process:**
   - assess effectiveness of process and its application
   - draw lessons for future investments
   - propose improvements to process
   - communicate results.

Figure 4. RAMP process

life-cycle of an investment as indicated below.

- *Process launch:* conducted early in the investment life-cycle.
- *Risk review:* conducted before key decisions or at intervals.
- *Risk management:* conducted continually between risk reviews.
- *Process close-down:* conducted at the end of the investment life-cycle or on premature termination.

Each activity is composed of several *phases*, each of which is made up of a number of process *steps*. The first and last activities – process launch and process close-down – are each performed once only, around the start and end of the investment. There are a number of risk reviews carried out at crucial stages or time intervals within the investment life-cycle. Risk management activities are performed continually between risk reviews based on the analyses, strategies and plans produced by the preceding risk review. The process launch will normally be part of (or shortly followed by) the first risk review, and the process

close-down will be part of (or shortly follow) the final risk review.

Although the process launch is generally undertaken in full only once, early in the life of the investment, it is likely to be necessary to reconsider and revise its results and objectives during subsequent risk reviews and risk management activities – e.g. to reflect changes in investment objectives or other circumstances, possibly arising in response to risk analyses.

Successive risk reviews and risk management activities will change in scope and focus as the investment progresses through the various stages in its life-cycle. At each review, risks whose exposures have ended will be eliminated from the analyses and plans, and their contingency provisions released; otherwise, each review will focus on future risks in the remaining stages of the investment (and not just the risks in the current stage).

Risk management does not end with the construction of a project. Often the revenue risk – the risk that the net revenue stream may differ substantially from that which has been predicted – has a great impact on the viability of the project

Table 2. Key documents covering the four activities of RAMP

Activity	Key document
Activity A: Process launch	RAMP process plan Risk diary (used in each activity)
Activity B: Risk review	Risk review plan Risk register (including assumptions list and residual risk analysis) Risk response strategy Risk response plan Investment model runs Risk review report
Activity C: Risk management	Trend schedules
Activity D: Process close-down	RAMP close-down report

Figure 5. Organising for RAMP

RISK ANALYSIS AND MANAGEMENT FOR PROJECTS

and will therefore require more careful and continuing analysis than risks which would have a lower financial impact if they occurred.

The RAMP process is outlined in Fig. 4, and discussed in greater detail in Chapters 3 to 8. Appendix 9 sets out the process formally for ease of reference.

2.8 Flowcharts

The process is illustrated diagrammatically in the form of flowcharts in Appendix 10. These indicate the iterative nature of RAMP.

2.9 Key documents

As explained above, RAMP involves completing a number of key documents to record the analyses, plans and other results from the process as it progresses. The ten key documents used to cover the four activities of RAMP are listed in Table 2. A table describing the purpose, contents and uses of each of the key documents is given in Appendix 11. It is assumed that users will prefer to devise their own document formats.

2.10 Organisation

Every aspect of the investment cycle is exposed to some risk, and therefore many people will be involved in some facets of risk analysis and management. To undertake this effectively an appropriate organisational framework with a clear assignment of roles and responsibilities needs to be established. This organisational framework should recognise that the project will go through successive stages, including eventually the operating stage, and consideration should be given to the desirability of maximising the continuity of management throughout all these stages. Lack of continuity may result in a

catastrophic loss of expertise about the project and its risks, and the planned responses to those risks, however good the paper trail. Moreover, the initial analysis and decisions may well be better if those concerned believe that they may have to live with the consequences in future years.

As shown in Fig. 5 there are two main aspects of managing risks using RAMP.

- *Managing the RAMP process:* i.e. planning, implementing and supervising the process for risk analysis and management.
- *Managing actual risks:* i.e. deciding what response measures to adopt, and taking appropriate actions to respond to and control risks.

RAMP normally deals with risk from the perspective of the sponsor, who is the *risk owner* or acts for one or more investors or other *stakeholders* involved. There may be several other stakeholders, each with different perspectives and risk exposures, for example

- bank or funding agency
- central or local government
- developer
- other revenue generators (e.g. retailers, car park operators and advertisers)
- franchisees, concessionaires and contractors
- customers and the public at large.

The sponsor needs to be aware of the stakeholders and of their respective interests, and take these into account when considering how best to deal with each risk. Some of the other parties may be willing to accept risks at a lower price than the owner's estimate of likely cost. In fact one party's risk can be another party's opportunity. For example, a serious fire in a new hotel nearing completion could cause the owner serious delays and loss of potential business, but result in profitable further work for the contractor.

It would be possible for RAMP to be applied from the viewpoint of one of the stakeholders other than the sponsor, in which case some suitable modifications would need to be made to the organisational structure described below. In practice, however, it might sometimes be possible for the sponsor to share its own RAMP analysis with other interested stakeholders so that only a minimum of extra work is required in order to focus the analysis on the stakeholder's own objectives and risk profiles.

As a general principle, a particular type of risk should be the responsibility of the party who

- has the greatest understanding and competence in dealing with it
- has access to the most information about the incidence, timing and impact of the risk
- is best able to control it.

A crucial principle of RAMP is that a single named individual should be assigned to control each principal area of risk on behalf of the owner/client during implementation of the project. These are the *risk custodians*. They will usually be senior executives engaged in the mainstream management of the investment who are made accountable on behalf of the sponsor for managing risks within their designated areas of responsibility – typically, the project development director in the early stages, the project manager in the asset creation stage and the operator for the operating stage. However, additional or different risk custodians may be appointed to manage particular categories of risks, such as threats to planning consents, political risks, terrorism, financing problems or competitors' actions. The risk custodians are required to review regularly all significant risk exposures and impacts, suggest appropriate response measures, and manage residual risks within their assigned areas, keeping the risk process manager up to date with developments.

To initiate and manage the RAMP process it is necessary to appoint a *risk process manager*, who will

- plan and launch the RAMP process
- lead individual risk reviews and ensure that the risk analysts (if more than one), who carry out the project appraisal, cover the whole field of potential risks between them without any gaps
- co-ordinate and monitor risk management measures
- report on progress in risk management
- draw lessons from experience in using RAMP to improve future RAMP initiatives within the organisation.

The risk process manager – ideally someone who is not performing other roles for the investment – should be appointed at an early stage in the life of the investment so as to ensure effective and consistent application of the RAMP process from the outset. Depending on the size and complexity of the investment, the risk process manager could be full or part time, and possibly an external consultant.

Any possible cultural impediments to the successful implementation of RAMP need to be carefully considered when devising the organisation structure and the arrangements for dealing with risk. If it is anticipated that there may be bias on the part of some people (for example, those who may wish to see the project proceed for personal career reasons irrespective of risk), the organisation structure needs to correct for this as far as possible. One way of doing this might be to introduce an independent audit of key figures used in the appraisal. It may even be sensible for the whole of the RAMP process and investment appraisal, as applied to a particular project, to be subject to independent audit before a decision is made. The organisation structure also needs to take account of the possibility that a dominant individual, even if he or she is not biased, may

unduly affect brainstorming sessions and
unwittingly cause them to be sub-optimal, perhaps
leading to serious consequences. It is essential that
the RAMP process is controlled by someone having
sufficient expertise and experience and, if this is not
available in-house, an external consultant can
provide it as well as introducing an element of
independence which may lead to greater objectivity.

2.11 Simplified version of RAMP

A simplified version of RAMP can be applied for the
preliminary analysis of a project or for the full
analysis of a smaller project. Details are set out in
Appendix 7.

3 Launching the RAMP process

3.1 Defining the RAMP strategy

This chapter is the first part of the description of the RAMP process, which is continued in Chapters 4 to 8 and set out more formally in Appendices 9 and 10. The first task is to confirm the perspective from which the risk analysis and management is being carried out and identify the principal stakeholders interested in the outcome. This version of the RAMP process assumes that risk is being considered from the viewpoint of the owner (i.e. the party which makes and owns the investment). The process can be adapted to suit other interests. Other stakeholders could typically include major shareholders, joint venture partners, the government, bankers, insurers and contractors.

A risk process manager will be appointed, who will plan, lead and co-ordinate the risk analysis and management process, and report on its results (see Section 2.10). In addition, the risk process manager's reporting line will need to be established to ensure firm accountability. His or her initial task will be to prepare a *RAMP process plan* which deals with all the matters in this chapter.

A preliminary brief on the objectives, scope and timing of the investment, including an assessment of its value and importance to the sponsoring organisation, and its complexity, should be prepared at this stage. This step is of the greatest importance. If the project proceeds, it will be rather like starting a new business, even if there is no intention of managing it separately from the sponsor's other business, with a large up-front cost followed by many years of operation in which the gross revenues less operating costs must pay for the initial capital cost and also provide a positive financial return to the sponsor. In practice there will usually be strong links between the decisions which are made in the early months of the project and its eventual financial viability once it reaches the operating stage. The key objective will not usually be to construct the asset on which the project is based at minimum cost and in the shortest possible time, important though that may often be, but to achieve eventual financial viability despite an uncertain future. The more flexible the design of the asset can be, catering for a variety of possible future uses, the more likely it is that financial viability will be achieved, even if key factors turn out quite differently from what was foreseen in the initial appraisal. Even if a flexible design involves a higher capital cost, this may well be worth it in the long run. The key performance indicators for the investment should be identified, and the method by which they will be checked as the project proceeds. These will include not only financial results but also other indicators – e.g. safety of staff and public, customer satisfaction, etc. The brief should include the definition of the provisional overall strategy for risk reviews and management throughout the investment life-cycle, including each of the following:

- *Purpose of RAMP:* what are the objectives of the RAMP process as applied to this investment (e.g. what key decisions or actions will depend on the results)?
- *Level of risk analysis:* what level of detail, sophistication and effort is appropriate for such an investment/project, given its type, value, complexity and importance?
- *Scope of review:* what stages in the investment life-cycle, or more specific aspects of the investment, are to be considered (if a comprehensive approach is not required)?
- *Stage/timing:* at what points or times within each stage are the risk reviews to be carried out?

- *Budget for RAMP:* establish a budget for conducting the RAMP process stage-by-stage for the life of the investment – or at least for the early stages.

It is essential that the risk analysis and management strategy be communicated as fully as possible to all concerned. The involvement of as many of the relevant people as possible will make it more effective.

Next a RAMP process team will be formed by identifying and assigning those who will act as *risk analysts* to identify risks, help to evaluate them and devise suitable responses. Depending on the level of RAMP analysis intended, there may be one or a number of people required to act as risk analysts. Ideally, the most appropriate key executives or specialists within the organisation, and appropriately qualified and experienced external experts, should be assigned the task of identifying risks for each stage of the investment life-cycle or principal activity within a stage.

The risk process manager should introduce and maintain throughout the RAMP process a *risk diary* in which to note:

- significant events in planning and executing the RAMP process
- problems encountered
- perceptions about major unresolved uncertainties
- valuable contributions towards the success of the investment or the review
- major results of the review (by cross-referencing any other documents produced)
- unforeseen risks which arise
- ideas for improving the review and its management.

3.2 Establishing the baseline

The baseline consists of the objectives, and the underlying assumptions, information and plans,

which underpin the evaluation of project risk and its subsequent management. This involves determining the information outlined below. The level of detail at this stage depends on the scale and complexity of the investment, but each item in the following list should be covered.

- *Investment definition:* what are the aims, scope and timing of the investment?
- *Objectives:* what are the specific objectives and key 'deliverables' of the investment? The objectives need the most careful consideration and definition right at the outset; they will often be more extensive than appears at first sight. A failure to define the objectives fully may well result in a failure to identify the risks properly.
- *Key parameters:* what are the financial and other parameters which define or affect the objectives in each stage of the investment life-cycle? Examples include: values over time of capital cost, revenue, operating and maintenance costs. These values should include effects on other investments/projects and other company operations.
- *Overall measure (or measures) of investment:* in this description of the process the overall measure is assumed to be whole-life NPV, but there are numerous alternative measures which may be considered more suitable in some situations, including: IRR, payback period, annualised rate of return, cost/benefit ratio. 'Real option techniques' may also sometimes be applicable.
- *Investment life-cycle:* what are the stages and sub-stages in the investment life-cycle?
- *Principal activities:* what are the main, separate activities in each stage of the life-cycle, how are they related, and how do they impact on each parameter and 'deliverable'?
- *Asset components and factors:* what are the major components of the asset to be created,

what are the principal factors affecting the project, internally and externally, and how are these related?

- *Baseline plans:* what are the investment strategy, organisational framework, master programme, funding arrangements and business plan for carrying forward the investment?

- *Underlying assumptions:* what are the main assumptions on which the investment/project objectives, strategy and plans are based? These should be listed in an assumptions list in which additional entries will be made as the work progresses.

- *Investment model:* what is the financial model which defines how the key investment parameters interrelate and impact on the overall measure of value for the investment? The model should include allowances for the effect of the investment on other investments and operations of the organisation. It should also (where appropriate) take account of the magnitude and timing of the effects of inflation, taxation and currency fluctuations.

- *Discount rate:* what should be the discount rate used to assess the NPV?

- *Initial values and cash flows:* what are the values and cash flows assumed for each key parameter associated with each activity in each stage of the investment? It is of crucial importance that these are estimated as accurately as possible, using evidence from past experience or similar projects wherever practicable, and they should be independently checked. Any significant bias, mistakes or omissions here will invalidate the rest of the work.

- *Initial overall value(s):* using the investment model with the initial values and most likely cash flows, compute the initial whole-life NPV and undertake a sensitivity analysis to derive the variability in its value which could result from potential changes in the values of the individual parameters. Tentatively identify those parameters where variations in their value are most likely to cause a large change in the whole-life NPV of the project, so that these parameters can receive sufficient attention at later stages.

3.3 Reviewing the process launch

Although the process launch is generally undertaken in full only once, early in the life of the investment, it is likely to be necessary to reconsider and revise its results and objectives during subsequent risk reviews – for example, to reflect changes in investment objectives or other circumstances. It will also be a useful reference point after the project has finished, when the RAMP close-down report is written.

4 Starting the risk review

Chapters 4 to 8 show how RAMP is implemented stage by stage. This chapter explains how the risk review – the process for systematically identifying and evaluating risks – is carried out. Chapter 5 shows how responses can be made to some of the risks, while Chapters 6 and 7 explain how the remaining risks which cannot be eliminated may be managed. What happens when the project comes to an end is shown in Chapter 8.

Risk reviews will be performed at crucial stages or time intervals in the investment life-cycle. The process activity for the first full review is described below. Subsequent risk reviews will revise and update the analysis and resultant actions as appropriate at the time of the review.

4.1 Planning and initiating the risk review

The risk process manager and the risk review team should be confirmed (or appointed) for this review. The purpose, scope and level of the risk review will need to be decided. This involves determining the following.

- *Specific aims of this risk review:* how are results of the risk analysis and responses to be used (e.g. what key decisions or actions will depend on them)?
- *Scope of review:* what stages or aspects of the investment are to be considered (if a comprehensive review is not required)?
- *Stage:* what is the stage reached in the investment/project life-cycle when the review is being performed?
- *Level of risk analysis:* what degree of detail, sophistication and effort is appropriate?

The next step is to plan the review by

- compiling an action plan
- defining resource requirements
- establishing a budget and timetable.

The above information, together with the aims, scope and level of analysis and the staffing and organisation for the risk review, comprise the *risk review plan*. All of the other parties likely to be involved in the review should be briefed about its purpose and timetable and the identities (names and roles) of those who will be participating in the review.

4.2 Identification of risks

The aims of this phase of RAMP are to

- identify, as exhaustively as practicable, all significant types and sources of risk and uncertainty associated with each of the investment objectives and the key parameters relating to these objectives
- ascertain the causes of each risk
- assess how risks are related to other risks and how risks should be classified and grouped for evaluation.

This is clearly a crucial phase. If a risk is not identified it cannot be evaluated and managed. The process of searching for and responding to risks is iterative. First each risk analyst attempts to list the downside risks associated with each objective, key parameter, major 'deliverable' or principal activity within that risk analyst's area of focus. It is essential that every relevant aspect of the investment is analysed by the team of risk analysts. The first attempt should be from first principles without the use of any checklist or other prompts, to avoid constraining the process of discovery. The resulting risks are listed in the risk register.

After this the risk analysts should repeat the exercise with the help of a downside risk matrix (Appendix 3) and generalised checklists (see pages 87 and 106) as well as other prompt aids such as:

- checklists of problems from: previous similar investments and projects, other case studies, technical papers, safety reviews and environmental impact studies
- site visits
- review of baseline plans, other key documents and outline designs.

Resulting risks should then be listed in the risk register for subsequent review and analysis, with a tentative indication of the significance of each risk ('clearly significant', 'possibly significant' and 'probably insignificant') and inter-relationships between risks. 'Significant' is to be interpreted as implying a risk, the potential consequence of which could have a significant effect on one of the objectives, parameters or 'deliverables', even if it has only a small probability of occurrence. At this stage, no risks should be eliminated or ignored, because even seemingly minor risks can combine to have a major impact.

Some or all of the risk analysts, and others who can make a valuable contribution, are next brought together for a brainstorming session to review the risks previously identified and to flush out further risks. Brainstorming should be in two parts. The first starts from scratch without any indications of the risks identified by the risk analysts. The second starts with the risks listed in part one and those listed by the risk analysts, and attempts to find additional risk exposure with the aid of a risk matrix and any other appropriate prompt lists. Participants should be encouraged to mention even seemingly unlikely downside risks and scenarios. The aim should be to create an open and genuinely explorative atmosphere, where no-one feels that their suggestions are undervalued or ignored. The risk register is extended and revised in the light of the results of the brainstorming.

It may be appropriate to interview or commission experts in particular aspects of the investment to identify risks which might otherwise be overlooked or not understood. It might also be useful to search relevant literature describing case studies of similar investments at home and overseas, to learn about the risks encountered and the mitigation measures and responses adopted. Again, any resulting risks are entered in the risk register.

Having identified as many downside risks as practicable in this phase of the review, it is necessary to classify and if appropriate group risks to assist in their evaluation. This is done by considering each risk in the risk register in turn to determine and record

- possible cause or causes of the risk
- trigger events giving rise to the occurrence of the risk event
- possible timing and potential frequency of occurrence
- the evidence for the existence of the risk, the trigger events, the timing and frequency of occurrence, and the forecast impact on cash flows (referring to past experience wherever practicable and appropriate)
- range of possible consequences – both physical and financial
- asset component, factor or activity associated with the risk
- objective, 'deliverable' or parameter affected
- other related risks
- form of relationship with other risks (e.g. common causes, one risk depending on occurrence of others, timing sequence of risks or causes or activities to which the risks relate)
- who currently owns the risk (e.g. the party who controls or is directly affected by it)

RISK ANALYSIS AND MANAGEMENT FOR PROJECTS

- the initial responses to the risk (e.g. what would be the first ideas on how to mitigate or respond to the risk – it may not be the most effective response but later analysis will discover that)
- whether there are any risks which should be eliminated because they duplicate or overlap with each other.

The analysis and understanding of risk groupings and relationships is often aided by representing them in the form of precedence, influence, risk/response or other diagrams, which should be appended to the risk register with suitable cross-references. A separate and crucially important part of the exercise is to check that the assumptions list, drawn up when the RAMP process was launched, contains all the underlying assumptions which have been made, possibly unconsciously, by participants in the risk identification process. Any new assumptions identified at this stage should be entered into the assumptions list.

Upside risks need to be identified also – i.e. events which could cause a more favourable outcome than expected. An example would be the possibility that revenue from traffic over a new toll-bridge might turn out to be better than anticipated. Greater efficiency than expected might be achievable, perhaps by reducing operational failures. A more favourable financing structure than expected might be devised if specialist advice is obtained. Possible actions to increase the chances of such outcomes and to maximise their impacts if they occur should be tentatively identified in the brainstorming sessions. To avoid confusion it is probably desirable to have separate brainstorming sessions for downside and upside risks, but the methodology is very similar. Some organisations completely separate the search for upside possibilities from the analysis of downside risk, but an integrated approach to upside and downside

risks is preferable, since any actions identified as responses may have both upside and downside consequences. Upside risks should be entered in a separate section of the risk register, showing the same information as for downside risks.

4.3 Evaluation of risks

For each identified risk which has a 'clearly significant' or 'possibly significant' consequence if it occurs, it may be convenient to assess in the first instance, qualitatively and approximately, the values described below:

- The likelihood/frequency of the risk occurring per unit of time or some other convenient unit (i.e. will it occur once in every week, month, year, 10 years, 100 years, etc.). We describe below some ways of expressing likelihood.
- The potential consequence (with respect to one or more of the parameters or related cash flows) if the risk occurs.
- The most likely frequency of the risk occurring during the whole lifetime of the investment.
- The likely timing of the risk's impact.
- The acceptance score, by combining the likelihood with the consequence, using risk assessment tables such as Tables 15 to 17 in Appendix 4.

Risk assessment tables have limitations, however, and they are not an essential step in the RAMP process. Because the 'score' they produce is a single measure of risk which does not take account of variability, some people believe they can be misleading. They should only be used as an initial sieve to identify some (but not all) of the downside risks requiring evaluation in greater depth. If these risks prove incapable of being sufficiently mitigated, then the whole future of the project may be in doubt and it may not be worth analysing the less serious risks.

37

The likelihood (or probability) of a risk event may be expressed in several ways:

- a once and for all chance of occurrence
- an average rate of occurrence over the duration of the investment
- a variable rate of occurrence
- a physical extent of occurrence (e.g. per kilometre of rail track)
- a probability of each of a series of possible values or ranges of values over the life of the investment (i.e. a probability distribution).

It is important to start with a natural or convenient basis for estimation, and link this to a life-cycle estimate. If there is a range of possible values, it may be acceptable, provided the range is not too wide, to represent the range by its mid point or average value. If this is not satisfactory, a range of values may be quoted – e.g. likelihood between 0.2 and 0.4, and consequence between £1 million and £1.5 million, and hence expected value between £0.2 million and £0.6 million.

If a risk is related to one or more other risks – in the sense that they share common causes or for other reasons the occurrence of one affects the likelihood of another – the related risks should be evaluated together. An example would be the risk of extra time being needed to construct the physical asset on which the project is based, which would be closely linked to the risk of a capital cost over-run. If the risks are not related – i.e. are independent, they can be evaluated separately. The resulting assessment of each risk or group of related risks should be entered in the risk register.

The risks that the assumptions set out in the assumptions list may not come true should be considered and evaluated in the same way as for other risks. It is very important to do this.

The significance of risks should be reviewed and then they should be reclassified into the categories

of significance. For risks which are 'probably insignificant', the decision must be made as to whether they can be ignored, covered within a general risk category or retained in the analysis. Examples of general risk categories are an overall allowance for possible causes of cost increases due to 'design development', 'commercial environment at time of tendering', etc. As a general rule, risks should not be ignored unless there is absolute confidence that they are trivial.

Particular attention and care must be taken with identifying and classifying risks which could have either

- serious or catastrophic consequences or high expected values, or
- exceptionally favourable consequences.

All the risks in both of these categories are likely to need particular, individual attention when assessing the overall 'riskiness' of the investment.

A decision must be made about which risks justify and are amenable to more detailed evaluation and quantification. Generally, these are the risks with largest expected values or, if probabilities are low, with most serious consequences. In choosing the risks for further analysis, it will be necessary to ensure that the likely benefit accruing from refining the estimate is worth the effort and cost involved. However, this does not apply to risks with catastrophic consequences (even if the probability of occurrence is thought to be low) as these are nearly always worth further study. For each such risk, a more detailed and quantified evaluation of likelihood, consequence, timing, expected value and dependencies must be conducted, noting carefully any assumptions made. Consideration must be given to the possibility that the likelihood of an event which would have catastrophic consequences may be significantly greater than the value which has been assigned to it.

A recommended method of doing this is that described by Chapman and Ward (2003) as the Simple Scenario approach, which develops subjectively a range of possible consequences and the associated probabilities. This applies a standard procedure to help suitably well-informed executives or experts to develop such a probability distribution systematically while minimising the tendency towards 'anchoring' and bias in the estimates. There are also other methods of scenario analysis, for example that used in Appendix 8. It should always be borne in mind that more extreme scenarios could arise in practice than the key scenarios selected for analysis. In addition, there are more sophisticated scenario identification techniques which may be used where a more rigorous approach is justified.

For each activity affecting each parameter of the investment, the RAMP team should compile an estimate of the potential impact of unexpected risks over the phases of the investment life-cycle, based on experience and the complexity and uncertainties associated with the activity and parameter. It may be appropriate to do this by identifying general categories of risks and making a contingency allowance for each based on previous experience in similar investments. The results should be entered in the risk register.

Using an investment model (Appendix 2) and parameter estimates, the overall impact of risks on the whole-life NPV of the investment (looking at both the range and dispersion of the simulated NPVs and the weighted average 'expected' NPV) should be determined. This may be achieved by calculating the NPV for each possible combination of risk impacts (i.e. all scenarios considered for the purpose of the analysis) or by producing a statistical distribution of the NPV using a computer-based Monte Carlo simulation, with different results depending on the assumptions used. Either way the result will be a probability distribution of the project's NPVs, showing the likelihood that each of the calculated NPVs will occur. Generally, the larger the potential financial outcome, the more serious the potential consequences of volatility in the estimated NPV, and therefore the more important it is to attempt to reduce the downside volatility, even though this is likely to be at the expense of a reduction in the expected NPV.

Since these calculations are based on no more than a series of estimated parameters, it is important to test the sensitivity of the calculations by substituting alternative values of the key parameters, including other plausible figures for the likelihood and impact of the principal risk events. This gives an idea of the degree of confidence one can have in the calculated probability distribution of NPVs and indicates the extent of the possible variation. Assumptions that various risks are independent or dependent may also be tested within this framework.

In calculating the NPV, it will often be appropriate to make a downward adjustment to allow for the likelihood of reduced revenues at certain times in the future on account of cyclical economic downturns.

A preliminary assessment will then be made of the extent to which the major downside risks can be mitigated – i.e. reduced, eliminated, transferred, avoided, absorbed or pooled – and the results will be recorded in the risk register. Details of the methodology are given in Chapter 5. The aim at this preliminary mitigation planning stage, however, will be limited to establishing whether optional courses of action exist which, on the face of it, may reduce the major risks to acceptable levels. If, in the case of a major risk, such options cannot be identified, consideration should be given at this stage to whether the project should be aborted or substantially modified.

An overall preliminary judgement should also be made as to whether the project looks like being sufficiently profitable to justify further analysis, having regard to the expected value of the NPV (after making a crude adjustment for the cost of the main mitigation options), the degree of confidence one can put in it, and other factors.

Assuming that there are good prospects for mitigating the major downside risks and that the project still appears likely to be profitable, the next stage is to proceed with planning risk responses in some detail.

5 Responding to risks

5.1 Introduction

Mitigating downside risks, or lessening their adverse impacts, is at the heart of the effective management of risk. Risk mitigation is an essential component of human behaviour because, in order to survive, most human beings tend to avoid taking reckless and uncalculated risks. Many normal day-to-day activities are affected by risk mitigation – e.g. the act of taking an umbrella when going out. Unfortunately in business activities risk mitigation is sometimes undertaken only at a rather superficial level. If more attention were paid to it, fewer business activities would end in disaster. It is not sufficient just to 'take a margin' for risk, since this results in little risk mitigation being done.

The other side of the coin is the need to optimise the possibility of favourable outcomes of the project, by taking appropriate actions. This, too, is fully catered for in the RAMP process.

The actions needed to mitigate downside risk and the actions needed to optimise upside risk are collectively referred to as 'risk responses'. We shall first consider the mitigation of downside risks (sections 5.2 to 5.10) and then the optimisation of upside risks (sections 5.11 and 5.12), leading to the formation of an overall risk response strategy (section 5.13). This is followed by a consideration of the residual risks remaining after the various risk response measures have been taken (section 5.14) and the investment decision (section 5.15).

5.2 The risk mitigation strategy

If implemented correctly a successful risk mitigation strategy should reduce any adverse (or downside) variations in the financial returns from a project, which are usually measured by NPV or IRR. However, risk mitigation itself, because it involves direct costs like increased capital expenditure or the payment of insurance premiums, might reduce the average overall financial returns from a project; this is often a perfectly acceptable outcome, given the risk aversion of many investors and lenders. A risk mitigation strategy is the replacement of an uncertain and volatile future with one where there is less exposure to adverse risks and so less variability in the return, although the expected NPV or IRR may be reduced. However, increasing risk efficiency by simultaneously improving the expected NPV or IRR and reducing the adverse volatility is sometimes possible and should be sought. Risk mitigation should cover all phases of a project from inception to close-down.

5.3 Ways of mitigating risks

There are four main ways in which downside risks can be dealt with within the context of a risk management strategy. Risks can be
- reduced or eliminated
- transferred (e.g. to a contractor or an insurance company)
- avoided
- absorbed or pooled.

There is also the question of whether it is worth carrying out research to reduce uncertainty.

Each of these ways of managing downside risk will be considered in turn, and the approach will be illustrated initially by examples drawn largely from the construction or asset creation stage.

5.4 Reducing or eliminating risks

This is often the most fruitful area for exploration. A crucial first step is to achieve effective mitigation of the strategic risk of an incorrect appraisal, referred to at the end of section 2.3, and only then should one go on to other areas. For example, could the design of the assets be amended so as to reduce or eliminate either the probability of occurrence of a particular risk event or the adverse consequences if it occurs? Or could the risks be reduced or eliminated by retaining the same design but using different materials or a different method of assembly? For example, if there is a manufacturing process which uses a chemical that could injure human health, the risk could be eliminated by changing to a safe chemical instead. Other possible mitigation options in this area include: a better labour relations policy to minimise the risk of stoppages, training of staff to avoid hazards, better site security to avoid theft and vandalism, advance ordering of key components, noise abatement measures, good signposting, liaison with the local community, locating staff in more than one building, etc.

5.5 Transferring risks

A general principle of an effective risk management strategy is that commercial risks in projects and other business ventures should be borne wherever possible by the party which is best able to manage (and thus mitigate) them. Contracts and financial agreements are the principal way in which risks are transferred. The use of contracts in this way is discussed in Section 9.10. It may be worth considering the use of companies specialising in risk transfer. Another possible way to transfer risks is to pass them to an insurance company which, in return for a payment (premium) linked to the probability of occurrence

and size of hazard associated with the risk, is obliged by contract to offer compensation to the party affected by the risk. Insurance cover can range from straight insurance for expensive risks with a low probability (e.g. fire), through performance bonds, which ensure that the project will be completed if the contractor defaults, to sophisticated financial derivatives like hedge contracts to avoid such risks as unanticipated losses in foreign exchange markets. Insurance is discussed in greater detail in Appendix 5.

To illustrate how insurance can help to improve a sponsor's risk profile, consider the following highly simplified example. Suppose that a project has a positive NPV of between £20 million and £60 million, depending on the outcome of various events. In addition, however, there is a 2% risk that a specific event will occur during construction, which would cost £90 million. If this were to happen, the result would be a reduction in the NPV of the project to a figure between minus £70 million and minus £30 million; in other words, there would be a substantial net loss on the project.

Now suppose that an insurance company offers to cover this risk for a single premium of £4 million. Most sponsors would probably consider this a worthwhile course of action, because it would change the risk profile to one where there was no possibility of loss but an expected positive NPV of between £16 million and £56 million.

5.6 Avoiding risks

The most obvious way of avoiding a risk is to avoid undertaking the project in a way that involves that risk. For example, if the objective is to generate electricity but nuclear power stations, although cost-efficient, are considered to have a risk of producing catastrophic consequences that is thought too high, even after every precaution has been taken, the practical solution is to turn to other forms of fuel to avoid that risk. Another example would be the risk that a particular small contractor would go bankrupt. The risk could be avoided by using a well-established contractor instead for that particular job.

5.7 Absorbing and pooling risks

Where risks cannot (or cannot economically) be eliminated, transferred or avoided, they must be absorbed if the project is to proceed. There normally needs to be sufficient margin in the project's finances to cover the risk event should it occur. However, it is not always essential for one party alone to bear all the absorbed risks. Risks can be reduced by pooling them, possibly through participation in a consortium of contractors, when two or more parties are able to exercise partial control over the incidence and impact of risk. Joint ventures and partnerships are other examples of organisational forms for pooling risks.

5.8 Reducing uncertainty

The above discussion of the mitigation options assumes that all the risks are known and can be quantified reasonably accurately. In practice, however, this is often far from being the case. Usually there will be a degree of uncertainty about which risks might occur that could significantly affect the project. Very often there will be uncertainty about the likelihood and impact of some of the major risk events which have been identified. One of the options in such circumstances may be to carry out research in order to reduce the extent of the uncertainty. Such research should be properly focused and costed: however, once it has taken place, it is a 'sunk cost' which should not figure in the capital cost of the project for purposes of analysis. A feasibility study

is a classic example of such research.

Take as another example a proposal to erect a new building in London on the site of an existing one which is to be demolished. The new building will need much deeper foundations than the existing one. Preliminary calculations suggest that the financial viability of the project is likely to be critically dependent on the capital cost of the new building, which in turn will depend to a large extent on how easy it is to construct the foundations. An obvious option, in order to reduce uncertainty, is to arrange for the site to be investigated at the outset by studying maps of underground rivers, water mains, gas pipes, cables and railways, and perhaps by drilling below the floor of the existing basement to take soil samples. Such action will not reduce the true underlying risks associated with the foundations but it may well reduce uncertainty sufficiently to enable the project to proceed. Some other ways of dealing with uncertainty are discussed in Appendix 1.

5.9 Mitigation of non-construction risks

Construction is only one relatively short phase in the total life of a project, which extends from the first identification of the opportunity, through appraisal, planning and preparation to design, construction, operation and then close-down. Although the asset-creation stage is clearly important, risks exist in all of the other phases of the project and are often of greater significance. Many projects have been relatively robust with respect to construction risks but have been totally compromised by shortfalls in operating revenues. Some of the non-construction risks which could arise at the operating stage include:

- inadequate forecasting of revenues
- fraud
- high operating costs due to high maintenance

- higher than expected costs of renewals of major equipment
- competition from other operators eroding market share and therefore revenues
- natural disaster (e.g. hurricane or earthquake)
- product obsolescence
- managerial incompetence
- reduction in use due to economic downturn
- unexpectedly high costs on termination of the project.

There is no feasible all-inclusive list of risks available, because new risks are arising all the time. Brainstorming sessions are essential to identify all risks which might arise as far as possible.

Mitigation measures which might be taken to tackle the various risks outlined above vary. For some risks an appropriate mitigation strategy is obvious. All forecasts should be independently checked, with validation against the known outcomes for comparable projects. Natural disasters are best insured against. Fraud by employees is best prevented, by having tight and effective financial control systems and can also be covered to some extent by insurance. The risk of high maintenance costs might be mitigated by changing the balance of capital to current costs in the specification of the construction of the project, thus 'over-engineering' the project. For some of these risks – product obsolescence or competitive pressure, for example – there may be no appropriate mitigation strategy: they are normal commercial risks and although they could in theory be insured against, the premium would be prohibitively expensive.

5.10 Use of financial structures to share risks

Various sources of funding are traditionally associated with different types of risk. Hence

providers of each category of funding tend, through experience, to be comfortable with certain categories of risks. Conversely, when asked to price unfamiliar risks, funders are likely to adopt a very conservative view, often simply the worst-case scenario. A bank, for example, is likely to take a very conservative view of the future sales of a product to be manufactured at a new factory which it is being asked to finance. The manufacturer, however, is relatively well versed in market risk for the product, and is in a much better position than the bank to understand the risk and will value it appropriately. Consequently, not only the ability of each party to manage and bear the cost of each risk should be considered, but also the value that each party attaches to carrying the risk should be borne in mind when allocating risks.

5.11 Optimising upside risks

A successful strategy for optimising upside risks should lead to actions which increase the chances of upwards variations in the financial returns or other outcomes from the project. However, like the mitigation of downside risk, the optimisation of upside risk will often involve direct costs such as increased capital expenditure, delay or the employment of additional resources which may be idle part of the time. Again there is a need to consider all phases of the project from inception to close-down. Some of these actions to optimise upside risks might also have the effect of increasing or reducing downside risks, so it is important to ensure that, where this occurs, there is appropriate feedback to the mitigation programme for downside risks.

5.12 Ways of responding to upside risks

There are ten main ways of responding to upside risks:

- *Increase the project's scope*: seek out sources of extra revenue, including finding alternative uses for the asset at times when it will not be fully employed for its primary purpose (for example, using school facilities outside school hours).
- *Improve the asset's design:* enable the asset to accommodate alternative or additional uses and facilitate eventual disposal.
- *Maximise expected revenues:* one example would be to design the asset in such a way that the market can be segmented and differential pricing introduced.
- *Relax the perceived constraints:* find ways through inappropriate rules, funding limitations, outdated prohibitions, preferences for certain firms as subcontractors, etc.
- *Reduce expected capital costs and timescales:* this may necessitate increasing the resources allocated to the project, removing bottlenecks, or even shortening the expected time for obtaining planning permission by paying compensation above market value to people adversely affected.
- *Reduce expected ongoing costs and operational failures:* for example by improving the design or by installing additional equipment or spare capacity.
- *Extend the project's expected life:* one way might be to make the design more flexible, which would enable the asset to be changed in future to exploit new opportunities or meet new constraints.
- *Seek the best financial and tax structure:* obtaining expert advice at an early stage.
- *Transfer upside risks to another party which is better able to manage them:* this might be done by giving third parties the option to construct additional facilities at their own expense, with a sharing of the rewards. Perhaps part of the asset might be rented out. Another

option might be to share the responsibility for owning or managing the project with a partner which is better able to exploit the upside opportunities, possibly because of its greater expertise or because it can integrate the project with its own existing business.

- *Take no action.*

In each case consideration should also be given to the possibility of carrying out research to find better ways of handling the upside risks, although since research is often expensive and time-consuming, there may be practical limits to how much research can be done. One approach to research on upside risks is to concentrate mainly on two areas:

- those risks where only minimum research effort is likely to be needed and there is a real possibility of positive results
- those risks where an improvement would make a major difference to the NPV of the project – e.g. the revenue risk.

5.13 Developing a risk response strategy

Each response option for both upside and downside risks should be evaluated, assessing

- likely effect on risk, consequence and expected value
- feasibility and cost of implementing the option
- overall impact of each option on cash flows.

Often the cost of a response has to be incurred before – possibly long before – the benefits are felt. Indeed the benefits may never be certain, because it is often impossible to say whether the risk event would have occurred had the measure not been adopted. For example, installing a prominent burglar alarm might deter burglars but we will never be certain this has happened.

Sometimes risk responses generate secondary downside risks of their own, which need to be taken into account (and possibly mitigated). For example, the use of a safer chemical in a manufacturing process may carry the risk of supply problems if there is only one source. There is also the possibility of generating secondary opportunities which can be exploited.

The most effective option or options, including no action where appropriate, should be chosen and recorded (with reasons) in the risk register. (Care should be taken to ensure that any secondary risks are not ignored). An action plan should be drawn up for each option.

The scope for dealing with some risks as a group should be explored. For example, a number of risks may be dealt with simultaneously by placing a financial agreement for funding, a construction contract or an operating franchise, or by finding a means of accelerating the completion of the last activities before an asset becomes operational.

Those risks which warrant an in-depth study of response possibilities should be selected. Generally these will fall into two groups.

• Those risks where there are apparently worthwhile response options but where confirmation is needed of the feasibility or cost of these options (e.g. that external parties are prepared to enter into commitments on the terms assumed).

• The residual risks which are potentially significant contributors to the upside or downside volatility of NPV but for which no satisfactory response measures have yet been identified.

The above should form the basis for a risk response strategy, comprising all of the actions and the associated implementation plans, and including a statement showing the costs and benefits of each response measure. The probability distribution

of NPVs can then be recalculated and consideration given to whether a better result can be obtained by excluding those response actions which have a high cost but limited beneficial effect on volatility. Some risks may need to be absorbed, with no action or only a partial response, because a complete response would be impracticable or too costly. The aim is to reach a state of risk efficiency if practicable, using a trial and error process.

Thus risk response is essentially a practical subject but a complex one, where there is a need for a methodical approach, clear thinking and imagination.

The principles of mitigation for downside risks can be illustrated by considering one particular area. Many large-scale computer projects have gone wrong in recent years (for example in the UK public sector, where some high-profile schemes have been abandoned or delayed, with vast cost and reputational damage). Some suggestions for risk mitigation in future schemes of this nature are set out in Appendix 6.

5.14 Residual risks

Residual risks are those remaining after response measures are taken. The RAMP team needs to assess the overall impact of residual risks by using the same techniques set out above. The results should be recorded in the risk register. Any new assumptions should be entered in the assumptions list. It is very important to ensure that the assumptions are comprehensively listed, including any implied assumptions. Consideration needs to be given to the risk of assumptions proving false and this vitally important step will necessitate further detailed analysis in the same way as for other risks.

The residual risks should be evaluated, making allowance for the result of adopting the selected response measures, and bearing in mind secondary risks and the cost of each measure. Their significance for each investment parameter can be determined by the use of judgement, or a technique like scenario analysis or Monte Carlo simulation, which can be used to estimate a probability distribution. The results of such research should be entered in the risk register, and are referred to as the residual risk analysis.

For each major activity in each stage of the investment life-cycle, an estimate should be compiled of the potential impact of unexpected risks, based on experience and the complexity and uncertainties associated with the activity. Unexpected risks include those foreseen risks which have not been measured or have been measured with a low degree of confidence. These should be consolidated into contingency allowances for unexpected risks.

Using the investment model, the overall impact of the residual risks on the investment (e.g. in terms of whole-life NPV) should be determined, with sensitivity analyses performed on the assumptions and estimates, and with account being taken of any contingency allowances.

With this data (expected value of the project's NPV, the estimated volatility, the reliability of its measurements, the results of the sensitivity testing and the potential consequences of the major risks), consideration must be given to whether the investment is still worthwhile or whether there is a version of the investment which would achieve (or nearly achieve) the same objectives with higher expected NPV and less downside volatility. The results of this work should be recorded in the risk response strategy.

5.15 The investment submission and decision

The investment submission on which the decision to proceed or not will be based should bring together:

- the business case for the project
- a description of the project and its baseline (see Section 3.2)
- a description of the most significant risks and how it is proposed to respond to them (see Section 5.13)
- a description of the residual risks and the effect they will have on NPV (see Section 5.14)
- if there are significant alternative options, a recommendation on which should be chosen
- a recommendation on whether the project should proceed
- matters outside the scope of RAMP.

The final stage is to obtain formal approval from the sponsor and any other key stakeholders (e.g. investors or lenders) for proceeding with the project. The decision-makers will take account of both the arithmetical results obtained and a range of intangible factors including:

- the extent to which approximation and 'guesstimates' have had to be introduced into the arithmetical work, leading to possible unreliability of the numerical results obtained
- 'political' and socio-economic factors
- the feasibility of the project and risk response actions
- any known biases on the part of those who have assigned numerical values to individual risks and the extent to which such biases may have been reduced by the introduction of checks and balances into the RAMP process
- the results of discussion with those closely involved in analysis of the risks of the project
- additional knowledge (if any) which was unknown to the risk process manager
- the extent of the remaining uncertainty
- intuition and experience.

Thus, despite all the care which will have been taken in a good project appraisal and risk

RISK ANALYSIS AND MANAGEMENT FOR PROJECTS

management process, it is still open to the decision makers to ignore the numerical results obtained and take a contrary decision based on wider considerations. While this is their prerogative, a contrary decision should never be made without the most careful and anxious consideration. In particular the reasons for the decision need to be fully documented to facilitate later investigation, should the decision turn out, with the benefit of hindsight, to have been incorrect.

In some circumstances 'real options' may influence the decision. These are options for further improving the sponsor's financial position, which are opened up by a decision to go ahead with the project or a decision to wait before going ahead with it. For example, in addition to the project's expected cash flows, it may be that the emerging experience and developing market conditions could generate further profitable opportunities but only if the initial project is undertaken. There is therefore a hidden contingent benefit in undertaking the project and this has a value. Suppose, for example, that a railway undertaking has to replace a number of bridges each year, and that expensive new equipment can now be hired which is expected to cut the time taken, but the project appraisal for the next bridge suggests that the time saved is not worth quite as much as the extra cost. Nevertheless, the project might be worth proceeding with, if it is felt that practical experience of working with the new equipment might lead to greater time saving thereafter in future bridge replacements. Another example of a 'real option' is the option to wait, rather than proceeding now with a project that has marginal financial viability, in the expectation that costs will reduce or benefits increase. Alternatively the project may be expected to be reasonably profitable but has excessive downside risk which

cannot be mitigated in the present state of knowledge, though emerging knowledge or new technology may well enable this downside risk to be mitigated if the project is undertaken later. Deferring a decision may have disadvantages but gives the sponsor the option to decide whether or not to proceed at a later date, and this option may have a value.

'Real options' are decision options which can be evaluated using standard decision analysis methods. Using scenario analysis in conjunction with an investment model, as shown earlier in this handbook, can help in the evaluation of these options, by applying estimated probabilities and impacts for the contingent effects of the anticipated improvements in key parameters and using sensitivity analysis where such estimates have a high degree of uncertainty.

An alternative way of making a decision about a project, in the case of a commercial company where the project is relatively large in relation to the size of the company, is to adopt a 'shareholder value approach'. This focuses on the company as a whole, taking a 'before and after look', and examining what difference in shareholder value would occur if the project were undertaken. The impact of the project on the company's net asset value, future earnings and debt cover would be calculated, allowing for the project's NPVs from the investment model, the risk responses which have been decided upon, and the extent of the residual risks. The less tangible issues to be evaluated would include the impact of the project on the company's ranking versus competitors, its impact on market perceptions of the company's management, its impact on the company's debt rating and its impact on the company's earnings cover and dividend policy. If the project would have a significant consequence for the way the whole of the company's business is perceived, this could fundamentally alter the share rating, which

might mean that the project would have a
financial effect on the shareholders which is more
extreme than the expected NPV of the project.
This method of looking at a proposed project
could lead to a decision which is quite different
from that which would be arrived at by just
looking at the project on its own. Although stock
markets are notoriously difficult to predict,
actuaries can help in the practical application of a
shareholder value approach in a particular case.

6 Planning for risk control

6.1 Risk response plan

Once the decision to continue with the project has been taken, a risk response plan is needed to minimise the probability of, and contain the impact of, all the remaining downside risks which cannot economically or practically be avoided, transferred or otherwise prevented. The other purpose of the risk response plan is to maximise the probability of occurrence of, and the impact of, all the remaining upside risks. For each residual risk or area of risk, as set out in the residual risk analysis, overall responsibility for the risk should be assigned to an appropriate 'risk custodian', with other parties possibly delegated with responsibility for monitoring and controlling specific risks within the risk response strategy. It should also be the responsibility of the risk process manager (or possibly one of the risk custodians) to monitor any changes which may be necessary in the key assumptions on which previous risk reviews have been based, as set out in the assumptions list.

In consultation with the risk custodians and other designated parties, the following should be devised:

- containment plans to minimise the downside risks and their impacts
- opportunity plans to maximise the upside risks and their impacts
- contingency plans to deal with specific residual risks should they occur, and for each of the 'trigger' events (or circumstances in which the contingency plans will be implemented), should be defined
- contingency budgets for the potential impact of the residual risks on each of the principal parameters of the investment.

It may be necessary to appoint the members of a 'crisis committee' to deal promptly with critical, potentially disastrous situations should they arise. Any restrictions of the committee members' level of authority should be carefully defined and reserve members should be appointed in case committee members turn out to be unavailable when a crisis arises.

The final step is to assemble containment plans, opportunity plans, contingency plans and contingency budgets into a risk response plan and seek the approval of the client and other key stakeholders for this.

6.2 Risk review report

At the end of the risk review, the risk process manager will critically assess the effectiveness of the review and the manner in which it was conducted, drawing lessons from the problems experienced and suggesting improvements for future risk reviews. This will be achieved, partly by reviewing the risk diary and other documents produced, and partly by discussion with the sponsor's representative and each of the other main participants. A formal risk review report should be compiled, outlining the results of the review – including the main risks and their likely effects, the overall riskiness of the investment, and the main lessons which have been learned.

The risk review report should be considered in detail by the sponsor's representatives responsible for the investment. In the light of the report, the sponsor will need to decide when the next risk review will take place and how it should be conducted.

6.3 Communicate strategy and plans

Finally, the relevant parts of the residual risk analysis, risk response strategy and risk response plan, relating to risks assigned to each risk custodian and other parties involved in executing the strategies and responses, should be extracted. The risk custodians and other parties involved in executing strategies and responses should be supplied with the appropriate extracts. Verification must be obtained that these have been received and understood, and that those concerned are committed to undertaking the required action. All those involved should be encouraged to comment on or make suggestions about the residual risk analysis, risk response strategy or risk response plan. If necessary, these documents should be revised to reflect the suggestions.

7 Managing risks

7.1 Implementing risk strategy and plans

A rigorous and comprehensive structure for implementing the risk strategy is essential if the strategy is to be carried out successfully. A lack of attention to this could result in the failure of the project or a failure to exploit significant upside potential.

The results of the risk review – notably, the residual risk analysis, risk response strategy and risk response plan – are used to manage risks as part of the mainstream management of the investment. However, it is essential that the risk analysis, strategies and plans continue to be monitored and updated regularly as risk exposures change and risk events occur in between risk reviews. The organisation and processes for doing this must be embedded in the procedures for managing the investment as outlined below.

The risk response strategy and the risk response plan must be fully integrated with the management systems and processes which determine the principal activities of the sponsor (whether these are concerned with investment, project management or the operation of a finished facility). It is vital that there is full accountability with single responsibilities and accountabilities assigned to named individuals for each action. In particular, it is important to ensure that there is effective follow-up to verify that the various plans and actions previously determined are implemented in a timely and satisfactory manner – e.g. that contracts, financial agreements and insurance policies are concluded, 'trigger events' are observed, and payments made.

It is also important that, where special or exceptional actions are needed to deal with risks which cannot effectively be integrated within the mainstream management processes, clear responsibilities and accountabilities should be assigned with reporting lines, or at least effective channels of communication, to the mainstream management. In addition, any exceptional actions, required to contain or respond to risks outside the scope of main management activities, must be co-ordinated with the main activities. Any significant changes or developments during the implementation of the risk response strategy and the risk response plan should be reported promptly to the risk process manager.

7.2 Monitoring and controlling risks

The key task at this stage of RAMP is the monitoring of risks included in the residual risk analysis, risk response strategy and risk response plan. It must be verified that the risk response plan is adequately resourced and effectively implemented. Other risks also need to be monitored regularly including those in the remaining stages of the investment life-cycle – not only the risks occurring in the present stage. Any significant changes in risk should be reported and assessed immediately. For example, the project may have to be abandoned half-way through construction if the risk that the facility may not be required increases sharply or if the risks in respect of operating revenue increase. Conversely there may need to be adjustments if new technology becomes available which could improve the NPV of the project. Care must be taken to ensure that there is a mechanism for identifying any new risks which may arise as a result of external developments.

Regular monitoring of risks can be undertaken by studying events, situations or changes (sometimes called 'trends') which could potentially affect risks during the normal management and progress of an investment. These trends can be exposed through

- site visits
- progress reviews
- design meetings
- correspondence
- negotiations with contractors
- ground surveys
- market research exercises
- tests
- study of new methods and technologies
- reports on other similar investments.

These trends must be systematically identified, analysed and monitored on a regular basis by scrutinising reports, letters, and notes on visits, meetings and telephone conversations. The results are entered in trend schedules. Ideally, these should be considered at regular progress meetings (say weekly) involving key members of the management team. The trends can be usefully categorised as

- *Potential (category P):* to be assessed or observed more closely.
- *Expected (category E):* mitigation or response measures to be taken.
- *Committed (category C):* measures taken and then either treated as changes to the investment baseline plans, after evaluating and allowing for their impact, or provided for in the risk response strategy or risk response plan.

At each subsequent progress review meeting, the 'trends' will be considered and may be eliminated

or moved into another category. Generally, newly identified 'trends' start in category P and then move first into category E and then into category C.

A serious danger to be guarded against is that this review process will, during the construction phase, give rise to late changes in the design of the asset which increase the project cost substantially. Many projects have suffered financial failure for this reason. There should come a point, before construction commences, where the design is frozen, except for changes which will not involve extra cost or unless there is the most compelling necessity. The authorisation process for any design changes which are sought after the design has been frozen should require authority to be obtained at a high level and should be accompanied by a full financial assessment of the consequences of the proposed change.

As progress is made through the investment life-cycle, it is necessary to revise the residual risk analysis, risk response strategy and risk response plan, and to release contingency budgets, as some risks materialise and other risk exposures change or disappear. When problems or significant changes in scope occur it will be necessary to revise some parts of the residual risk analysis, risk response strategy and/or risk response plan. Regular reports on progress, problems and changes should be submitted to the client's representative and other key stakeholders (notably the project manager and operations manager). The risk diary will be updated regularly by the risk process manager.

Finally, the fundamental merits of the investment – whether or not it is worthwhile – should be continually assessed and a risk review set in hand when events occur which appear to have significantly altered the risk profile of the project.

8 Closing-down phase

At the end of the investment life-cycle, or on prior termination of the project, a retrospective review will be made of the investment (in terms of its success and risk history) and of the contribution and effectiveness of the RAMP process itself as applied to the investment.

8.1 Assessing the performance of the investment

The risk process manager, in conjunction with the sponsor's representative, will first evaluate the performance of the investment, comparing its results with the original objectives. Using risk review reports and the risk diary, an assessment will be made of the risks and impacts which occurred in comparison with those anticipated, highlighting risks which were not foreseen or were grossly miscalculated.

8.2 Reviewing the RAMP process

The risk process manager will then critically assess the effectiveness of the process and the manner in which it was conducted for this investment, drawing lessons from the problems experienced and suggesting improvements for future investments. This will be done, partly by reviewing the RAMP process plan, risk diary, risk review reports and other documents produced, and partly by discussion with the sponsor and each of the other main participants.

At the time of the decision to proceed with the project, it may well be that it was recognised and accepted that there would be a number of residual risks. If some of these risk events subsequently occur, and the impact is as expected, this would not indicate a failure in the RAMP

process, though it might indicate a failure to control the risks in question adequately. If, however, the risk events which occur, or the size of their impacts, were not adequately foreseen (as evidenced by the risk register), this may suggest a need to make risk reviews for other projects more rigorous in future.

The results of the review will be recorded in a RAMP close-down report, which can be easily referred to for future investments. Copies of the report should be circulated to all parties involved and then signed off by every party as an agreed record of events.

8.3 Prematurely terminated projects

Some projects will be terminated as soon as the initial risk review has been completed, because the risk-reward ratio is not deemed to be sufficiently attractive, and other projects will be terminated before the end of their planned life-cycle because of adverse developments. The production of a RAMP close-down report as a guide for other projects is likely to be particularly valuable in these circumstances because the most critical events in the history of the project will have occurred recently.

9 Applications and case studies

9.1 Introduction

This chapter discusses the application of RAMP in practice. It illustrates the uses to which RAMP can be put, by reference to case studies. A summary of the key points which emerged from visits to practitioners in several large corporations follows and then a description is given of how RAMP can be applied to individual projects and to a series of projects. The importance of risk management and evaluation in public sector procurement, including Public-Private Partnerships and the UK Private Finance Initiative, is discussed. Next comes an indication of the scope for application of RAMP techniques in other circumstances, including concessions and franchise operations, and ongoing activities not involving the construction of physical assets. Finally, there are a few thoughts on how the RAMP process should influence, and be influenced by, considerations relating to the contracts which will be entered into by the various parties concerned with the project.

9.2 Hypothetical case studies

Some hypothetical case studies have been prepared to illustrate how RAMP can be applied in practice. The examples are necessarily much simpler than real-life exercises, but they demonstrate the general approach recommended and highlight some important points. They also show how the RAMP methodology can be integrated with suitable investment models, in order to evaluate the risks financially and thereby enable rational decisions to be made about risk responses and whether the project should proceed.

The first case study concerns the introduction of a new computer scheme at a company. The project is relatively small and a simplified application of RAMP is appropriate, in conjunction with an NPV investment model. The process is shown in Appendix 7. The project has potential upsides and downsides, and these are evaluated by straightforward scenario analysis. An option for the mitigation of downside risks is explored and it is shown what the financial effect would be on the various outcomes if this option were adopted. Whether the risks should remain unmitigated or not would, in this example, depend upon the sponsor's attitude to risks of this size.

In the second example the case being examined is the building of a tolled road bridge across a river estuary which is at present served only by car ferries. Two large towns are separated by the river and the new bridge will substantially reduce the journey time between them. There are three alternative sites for the new bridge. Details of this case study are set out in Appendix 8, which also illustrates how to apply an investment model.

A preliminary appraisal of the project proceeds by making some simple calculations, using the present ferry tolls as the tolls for the bridge. These calculations suggest that the project may be marginally viable for two of the possible sites but not the third. However, a high-level risk assessment results in the rejection of one of the two more favourable sites.

The team then identifies and analyses the risks, and a mathematical model is constructed to simulate the traffic flow expected in various circumstances. A risk response exercise leads to the conclusion that one of the principal options is to buy up the existing ferry company in order to prevent the bridge being undercut in price with a resulting loss of traffic. Buying up the ferry company has secondary risks and these are evaluated and a response plan developed for them.

This example highlights the following points.

- The need for high-level consideration of the project at an early stage, so as to reject unworkable options and save abortive work.

- The use of an iterative approach in the analysis, gradually getting into greater depth.

- The possibility that the earlier stages of risk analysis will lead to a change in the scope of the project in order to minimise risks.

- The fact that, although the calculations are an important input to the decision, a range of intangible factors must also be taken into account by the decision-makers.

- The use of scenario analysis and the need for the scenarios with the more serious potential consequences (even if they are unlikely to occur) to be specially considered.

- The use of group brainstorming to generate 'key scenarios' and risk response options.

- The need to analyse the 'secondary risks' which result from changes in the scope of the project or from the risk response options selected.

A more elaborate case study, illustrating the use of RAMP methodology and the scenario method, was set out in an article by one of the authors of this handbook (Lewin, 1996). This related to a hospital project and showed how the public sector could evaluate the net benefits of the project on the alternative bases of carrying out the project itself, or accepting the provision of a service by a private bidder who would make the necessary investment.

9.3 Lessons from company visits

Several visits were made by the authors in 1998 to large companies in order to see how they assessed their projects; sincere appreciation is expressed to those companies who helped in this way. The

organisations visited included Railtrack, Royal Dutch Shell, the Norfolk and Norwich NHS Trust, and the Highways Agency. They were not, of course, applying RAMP methodology itself, but they had somewhat similar processes in place and were able to give some useful hints which would be equally applicable to users of RAMP. These can be summarised as follows.

- It is essential to take proper account of the potential legal and business environments within which the project will exist.

- Worthwhile projects, for which workable solutions to problems exist, can be turned down because of poor methodologies which do not fully explore the needs, benefits and costs.

- Properly focused research, rather than simply extrapolating past data, can provide confidence for all parties when assessing the business case and specific proposals.

- The end users need to be committed to the project at an early stage, to prevent abortive work. All the decision-makers also need to be involved at an early stage.

- Using a well-constructed risk methodology can help to overcome the fears and reconcile the requirements of all the interested parties, and bolster their confidence in the project.

- The methodologies already in use, even by large organisations, sometimes do not fully meet RAMP principles and could usefully be overhauled.

- There is a need to consider the human factor in risk analysis and management and to guard against excessively optimistic or pessimistic assumptions. In particular one should be sceptical of estimates put forward by those who have a vested interest in the project proceeding or not proceeding. Some estimates may be distorted for reasons associated with the interaction between the personalities of the people connected with the project.

- Never rely completely on checklists – always have a brainstorming session as well, and ensure that no possibilities are ruled out.
- Risk workshops should contain a variety of people from different backgrounds.

If this last point needs underlining, the authors of the PRAM report (see Section 1.10) point out that perceptions of a specific risk will differ from one person to another, with specialists in particular domains sometimes underestimating risks within their speciality and overestimating risks outside it. Moreover, individuals may be wary of giving an honest and objective view of the extent of a risk, because they may feel they will attract ridicule or hostility which may possibly impact on their careers. A group decision about downside risk may be insufficiently cautious, because it can less easily be held to be the responsibility of any individual and no individual within the group wishes to be seen by colleagues to be unduly negative. The formal process may need to be modified to remove such elements of possible bias as far as possible.

9.4 Individual projects

The main practical question which needs to be determined in applying the RAMP methodology to individual projects is the degree of depth to which the analysis should be taken. The full version of RAMP presented here would normally be well worthwhile for a major project, say one involving a capital investment of £10 million or more, provided that preliminary investigations proved promising. There is no denying that carrying out the full version of RAMP could be expensive, but for a major project the cost pales into insignificance beside the likely benefits. For small or medium-sized projects a simpler version of RAMP can be used (an example of which is shown in Appendix

7). The main benefits of applying RAMP (in either its simple or full form) to an individual project are likely to include:

- improving the credibility of the business case for the project
- identifying new risk areas not previously considered
- making sure that serious and catastrophic risks are not inadvertently overlooked in the final stages of the analysis
- opening up the possibility of additional risk response measures
- focusing on the overall risk profile of the project and not just individual risks, leading to a better chance of reaching the right decision on whether to go ahead
- providing evidence about the residual risks, which will help to convince financiers to back the project
- giving better control of the risks once the project has been authorised.

9.5 A programme of projects

Sometimes a company will undertake a series of projects, each of which may be substantial in its own right but constitutes a relatively small part of the company's overall investment programme. The RAMP methodology is still applicable in such circumstances, although the company may be less averse to downside risk on any individual project, taking a 'swings and roundabouts' view. This may mean that the company would be less willing to consider risk mitigation measures which reduce the expected net present value of a project. It may also mean that some of the research work can be reduced, since the risks identified for one project may well be applicable to some of the other projects. In other ways, too, it may be possible to standardise the working methods with a resulting saving of expense.

Suppose, for example, that a rail company was undertaking a track renewal programme consisting of a series of similar projects at different locations. Clearly the programme as a whole would be likely to benefit from RAMP analysis, to identify and respond to the risks common to all the projects. Each individual project could then be the subject of a 'mini-RAMP' exercise, which would involve an examination of the risks specific to that particular project.

9.6 The Private Finance Initiative

Over the last 10 years in the UK, the government has sought to have much of the public sector's capital and infrastructure investment delivered through a developing form of procurement and contract known as the Private Finance Initiative (PFI). (A more recent form of this, applicable to some projects, is known as a Public-Private Partnership). Under the PFI, pubic sector bodies contract with private sector bodies that will provide a long-term service which involves (among other things) the need for long-term investment at the expense of the private sector contractor.

Negotiating these contracts is an essential part of the process and has as an overriding objective the achievement of 'value for money' for the taxpayer and the transfer of 'substantial' risk to the private sector contractor. There are two important public sector policy goals, which in effect serve as parameters on risk transfer:

• Achieving value for money for the taxpayer usually means that a given risk should be borne by the party which can assume and manage that risk most efficiently and effectively.

• Enough risk should be transferred to the private sector contractor to ensure that the asset created is capitalised on the contractor's balance sheet and not on the public sector's.

The PFI has heightened awareness of project risks in ways that public procurement hitherto has not been able to do, so that the identification, allocation and management of risks has grown to become an essential part of the PFI process.

A PFI contract is an agreement for the provision of services. For example, the requirement for a new hospital is defined as a requirement for clinical support services and for a prison as correctional services. This leaves the private sector free to determine the best form of investment to provide the required services, which may be a far more efficient or innovative way than the public body is capable of providing. The private contractor determines the best form of investment, which it will design, build, finance and operate in order to provide the service required by the public body. PFI contracts are typically let for long periods, often in excess of 25 years, in order to give the contractor time to recoup capital and make a profit.

For example, in a roads contract the private contractor builds and finances the road. It provides all services associated with the road, including all aspects of operation and maintenance, to the Highways Agency, which pays the contractor in the form of 'shadow tolls'. Roadside services, in the fields of leisure, catering and retailing, can be provided direct to the public by the contractor.

Hospital projects are quite different. The contractor provides an NHS Trust with a range of non-clinical support services, to be delivered in a hospital building which the contractor designs, builds, finances and operates. Clinical services continue to be provided by the Trust and therefore the two parties must work together effectively after the hospital comes into operation.

PFI projects are usually complex, requiring the interaction and integration of a multiplicity of agents, functions and time horizons. For example, the private contractor might be a loose consortium of organisations, operating together to provide the range of services required by the public body. Each of these individual organisations, and the public body itself, will have different corporate objectives, management structures, time horizons and risk profiles. A vast array of technical, legal, financial and organisational functions will need to be integrated.

Risk analysis and management is crucial to the success of PFI projects and the RAMP process can readily be used for this purpose by either the public sector body or the private contractor (or both). In fact there may sometimes be a good case for both the public sector body and the private contractor to agree fairly near the start of their negotiations that it would be sensible to obtain an independent RAMP analysis of the project as a whole, as a preliminary to sharing the residual risks between them.

During the negotiations on risk sharing the public body must evaluate the PFI bid and determine whether it offers better value for the public sector or the community as a whole than does the alternative of carrying out the investment and providing the service itself. Some of the key questions guiding this assessment follow.

- What is the expected net present value of the project to the public sector under each alternative?
- To what extent is the possibility of both downside and upside outcomes for the public body reduced if some of the risks are transferred to the private contractor?
- What risks would be retained by the public body and could they be successfully managed?
- Will the contractor be able to manage effectively the risks transferred to it and have the financial ability to do so? Is there a risk that the private sector consortium might break up?
- How can the best deal for the public sector be negotiated?

Lewin (1996) sets out a possible way of doing the necessary calculations using RAMP methodology.

The private contractor will no doubt wish to do its own assessment, and apply RAMP methodology in the same way as any sponsor would do for its own projects. In the risk identification phase, however, the contractor will wish to consider whether there are any special risks involved in entering into a long-term contract with the government over a period of many years, during which its political complexion might change significantly, and whether there are any ways of mitigating such risks.

Even if it has not proved possible to get an independent RAMP report which is jointly sponsored by both the public body and the private contractor, it will be useful to maintain a 'risk matrix' for the project. This expression is used in an entirely different sense from its meaning in the identification phase of RAMP methodology, and means in PFI negotiations an important working document which provides both parties with information on all identified and significant risks in the project and the current allocation of these at any given point in the negotiations. Before the PFI contract is finally agreed, both the public body and the private contractor will wish to consider risk response measures, and here again the RAMP methodology provides an appropriate way to proceed for each party.

Once a PFI contract has been agreed between the public body and its private contractor, each party will need to control implementation and its own risks, and this can best be done in the way which is recommended in the RAMP methodology. There is an additional dimension, however, in that there will need to be joint risk reviews regularly between the public body and the private contractor, to take account of emerging developments. It may be desirable to appoint an independent risk manager who will advise the project board on this.

9.7 Other public sector procurement

In 2003 the Government revised the Green Book which it uses as a guide for the procurement of goods and services throughout the public sector, apart from the special case of the PFI referred to in Section 9.6. In the Consultation Document which preceded the new Green Book, it was stated that the aim was to tackle the following deficiencies in the previous process:

- The methodology needed to be long-term and to tackle key issues, such as evaluation of benefits.
- There needed to be stronger incentives to encourage users to adopt a systematic and thorough approach to appraisal.
- There needed to be strengthened expertise in appraisal techniques within government.

The most striking change was a reduction in the discount rate used to appraise projects, from 6% to 3.5% per annum, declining to 1% per annum for projects with very long life expectancies. This has the effect of placing a greater value than previously on benefits received and costs incurred in future years, particularly in respect of more distant periods. Another change was that specific adjustments now have to be made in project appraisal to allow for 'optimism bias' – i.e. a systematic tendency observed in the past (see Appendix 12) for appraisers to be over-optimistic in assessing projects. These adjustments are based (loosely) on an analysis of past experience and make it more difficult for projects to pass the viability test on the basis of the assessed cash flows. However, if project appraisers can demonstrate that good practice has been adopted in effectively managing the downside risk areas, the adjustments may be reduced.

Whatever the merits of introducing an optimism bias may be for public sector appraisals in the UK, it is not a technique we recommend for general use outside the public sector, as it has some major disadvantages:

- The application of optimism bias adjustments may encourage project promoters to understate costs in an uncontrolled way.
- The size of the adjustments to be made will often be based on evidence which is too scanty to establish confidence that the adjustments are of an appropriate magnitude.
- If properly prepared, the cost estimates should already include variant figures which allow for risk, so that subsequent application of an optimism bias would result in double counting. If, however, the project appraisal is being based on single 'most likely' estimates of cash flows, then the risks are not being properly studied and opportunities for risk responses which might well improve the project out-turn are being lost.
- If the project goes ahead, the optimism bias adjustment will (in effect) provide the project manager with a large contingency allowance in his budget, so that the incentive for effective cost management is reduced.

We believe that (rather than applying an optimism bias adjustment) in general it is preferable to adopt an open and unbiased approach to project appraisal, with full discussion and documentation and with checks and balances, such as independent auditing of the parameters and models used, before key decisions are made. This will tend to ensure that the analysis is based on the most realistic figures that can be obtained, including estimates which are as realistic as possible of the extent of the upside and downside variability of these figures and the likelihood of such variations occurring. Even more important, detailed analysis, as described in this handbook, will facilitate the mitigation of downside risks and the maximisation of upside potential.

RAMP is recommended in the Green Book

(paragraph 10 of Annex 4) as a tool for risk management in the public sector. We hope that as RAMP becomes more generally applied in the public sector, and staff become more experienced in its use, the need to apply optimism bias adjustments will gradually diminish.

9.8 Concessions and franchise operations

Granting concessions and franchises allows a business to have access to greater resources, a wider skills base and new capital, while retaining some element of control. Although some franchises may be purely operating concessions without a need for investment, others may require the concessionaire to invest in plant and machinery or even infrastructure. In the latter case the contract may be for 20 years or more, to enable the concessionaire to recoup the cost of investment and make a profit. RAMP methodology is entirely applicable in such situations, both for the company granting the concession and for the concessionaire. For the company granting the concession, the risks include the possibility that the actions of the concessionaire will taint the business overall or that the concessionaire will become insolvent while owing the company money (perhaps while any initial financial assistance given to the concessionaire is still outstanding). The company will normally wish to mitigate at least the first of these risks as far as possible.

For the concessionaire, the amount of investment being made may not be sufficient to justify any more than a simplified RAMP analysis, but the need for that may be great, since the failure of the franchise operation will often have financial consequences which are very serious for the concessionaire, who may be very averse to major risks and wish to mitigate them as far as possible. Even if the concessionaire is making no investment at all, a full risk analysis and cash flow model will be necessary to set pricing.

9.9 Ongoing activities

The risk review, risk response plans and risk control processes described in this handbook are applicable to ongoing activities not involving the construction of physical assets. For example, a risk management exercise was conducted in the pensions management department at a major public company. The management team decided to assess the ongoing downside risks associated with the pension funds at home and overseas, with a view to adopting further risk mitigation measures where these could be financially justified.

The first step was for the management team to identify a list of downside risks. These ranged from fraud and crime, right through to the possibility of the administrative work getting behind because of a sudden shortage of resources or a sudden peak of work. The risks were then analysed, with members of the management team contributing their views on the probability or frequency of occurrence and the likely consequences if the risk event occurred. It was found that in practice most of the risks could be expressed as being 'likely to occur once every x years'. The next step was to classify the risks according to a risk assessment table with a view to prioritising the risks with the highest scores. Particular attention was paid to those risks which would have very serious consequences, even if the frequency of occurrence was estimated to be low.

Brainstorming sessions were arranged to discuss some of the options for mitigating these priority risks. This was perhaps the most valuable part of the whole process, in that a number of entirely new options for mitigation emerged, which had to be evaluated, having regard to the costs which would be incurred if they were adopted.

Where companies make annual reports to shareholders about the main risks facing the business, RAMP methodology may be helpful in those cases where it is possible to regard a company's business as an ongoing project or a series of ongoing projects, some of which may have reached the operations phase. An additional benefit is that the RAMP analysis could reveal some risk response options not previously considered, even for an ongoing business. It could also highlight those ongoing projects where (perhaps because of a change in the risk profile since original authorisation) the probability distribution of the net present values of the stream of future cash flows shows too high an overall risk to justify continuation of the project.

So how should one apply RAMP to an existing ongoing activity? The answer is that it is exactly the same as applying RAMP at the later stages of a project which has been the subject of RAMP reviews from the outset, except that there will be no previous baseline to which to refer. The essential additional step, therefore, is to establish that baseline, just as one would at the start of a new project (see Chapter 3). Part of the process necessary to the establishment of the baseline will be the collecting together of the various papers which have been put together in the past in relation to the activity in question, insofar as such papers are still relevant to the future of that activity. All the cash flows taken into account in the financial analysis should exclude cash paid or received in previous years: in particular, any capital which has been invested in the activity in the past is a 'sunk cost' which is irrelevant in assessing the NPV of future cash flows and the probability distribution of such NPVs.

In some cases, in relation to an ongoing activity, it may not be essential to carry out a detailed financial analysis and the aim will be to concentrate on risk (both upside and downside) and its management alone. If this is the case, it may nevertheless be necessary to carry out some approximate financial calculations when

considering an optimum package of risk response, to ensure that the costs involved are reasonable in relation to the benefits obtained.

9.10 Contractual arrangements

Once a project has been authorised, it is normal for the interests of the various parties to be defined by contractual arrangements. It is important to ensure that these arrangements take full account of the residual risks remaining after the response measures have been taken, and that responsibility for each of these risk events, should it occur, is clearly identified. This will necessitate the drawing up of quite detailed heads of agreement between the parties and close liaison with the lawyers involved.

There are, of course, many ways in which the contractual arrangements could be structured. One of the classic ways of ensuring that the project sponsor is relieved of both upside and downside risk is to enter into a fixed price contract, whereby the contractor undertakes to provide the sponsor with assets or a service at a fixed price (which may or may not be index-linked in future years). The reverse of this is a cost-plus contract, whereby the sponsor pays the contractor whatever the job turns out to cost, plus a fixed percentage for profit. It may be thought that the fixed price contract is necessarily preferable from the sponsor's viewpoint, but inevitably the contractor will build in a safety margin (except, for example, during an economic recession, when a contractor may take non-profit business to keep the workforce together) and the contract may therefore turn out to be more expensive than a properly supervised cost-plus contract would have been.

Moreover, even a fixed price contract may turn out to involve the sponsor in added cost. This is because such contracts usually include various clauses designed to cover exceptional circumstances, and in practice such clauses often result in negotiations towards the end of the construction period on whether an additional payment to the contractor is justified. Also there is usually a *force majeure* clause, under which the contractor cannot be held responsible for extra costs or loss of receipts arising from delays due to strike action or other actions deemed to be outside its control. Such risks need to be taken into account in the sponsor's RAMP analysis.

Where there is a long-term contract for many years, as is often the case if a concessionaire has paid for infrastructure, it is quite likely that totally unforeseen adverse circumstances may arise at some point. It may or may not be clear from the contract which of the parties must bear the responsibility for remedying the problem. Even if it is clear that the responsibility should rest with the concessionaire, it may be impossible for him to meet the extra cost without becoming insolvent, in which case negotiations with the sponsor will be sought to achieve a sharing of the extra cost. Such negotiations are also inevitable if the contract is not clear about who should meet the extra cost. This means that a long-term contract is always to some extent a true risk-sharing partnership between the parties, however closely the contract appears to define each party's responsibilities.

Even if, as is highly desirable, clear instructions have been given at the outset to the lawyers about the differing responsibilities of the parties for a variety of risks, it is essential to check the final draft of the contracts carefully, to ensure that extra risks excluded in the RAMP process have not been shown as the sponsor's responsibility. If they have, it may be necessary to rework the RAMP process somewhat, in order to check that the project is still viable.

Where one party is obliged under the contract to provide a service or facility which could imperil the project or the interests of the other parties if it is not delivered to the specified standards, the downside risks for the other parties may be mitigated by the inclusion in the contract of penalty clauses for non-performance. However, while such clauses may act as a deterrent to non-performance, they are not always effective in extracting the prescribed penalties and some residual downside risks for the other parties will remain.

10 Future development

10.1 Continuing development

The publication of this handbook is a first step in the development of the RAMP process, which has the potential to become an industry standard in the field of project appraisal and risk management. It is already achieving widespread recognition as a useful tool. However, to become even more useful, the RAMP process will be further developed and will continue to be regularly updated. Above all, it will need to learn from and build upon experience gained by its users. It is only by continuing dialogue (involving feedback) between users and developers of RAMP over time that RAMP can become a benchmark in its field.

10.2 Getting feedback

If sufficient numbers of RAMP users indicate that they would find it helpful, a continuing forum will be established, within which RAMP briefings and process development can continue. It will also be desirable to continue to supplement the RAMP handbook from time to time with updated material to enable the assimilation of new knowledge and understanding gained in application of the system. This will be done in the first instance through the RAMP website (www.RAMPrisk.com). The opportunity for dialogue with users could be reinforced with the establishment of a RAMP Help Line offering initial advice on a non-commercial basis to users of the RAMP system if there is sufficient demand for such a service. In the longer run it is possible to envisage RAMP becoming established as an example of 'best practice' for the appraisal of projects, with the development of a system of accreditation of practitioners which could provide assurance to would-be investors and other potential stakeholders. In the meantime the working party would very much welcome any feedback from users of this handbook (See Section 10.4).

10.3 Wider professional involvement

RAMP has been jointly initiated by the Institution of Civil Engineers and the Actuarial Profession. There are other professional disciplines involved in engineering, construction, business, property and finance with much to contribute on risk. Should it be decided to develop RAMP further, the founding bodies would see merit in involving other partners and professional groupings in the process. It can only benefit all, since risk management is becoming increasingly recognised as a key management discipline.

10.4 Contacting the RAMP working party

The RAMP working party can be contacted through any of the following:

- Institute of Actuaries
  Staple Inn Hall, High Holborn
  London, WC1V 7QJ
  Tel: 020 7632 2100
  Fax: 020 7632 2111

- Institution of Civil Engineers
  1 Great George Street, London SW1P 3AA
  Tel: 020 7222 7722
  Fax: 020 7222 7500

- By leaving feedback on the RAMP website
  www.RAMPrisk.com

Glossary

Assumptions list: this is a key part of the risk register which lists the assumptions, both explicit and implicit, on which the RAMP analysis is based. It is updated as and when previous assumptions need to be modified or new assumptions have to be made.

Baseline: the set of assumptions and methods which are used as the basis for the evaluation of risk in a project and its subsequent management. Risk analysis is impossible without a baseline which would, for example, include information on the objectives of the project, values of key financial parameters like discount rates, assumed levels of cash flows, financial model adopted, etc. (see Section 3.2).

Brainstorming: an intense and focused but spontaneous scrutiny of an issue. A brainstorming session, led by a 'facilitator', is used to encourage participants to put forward relevant ideas. In the context of risk, the purpose will be to generate as many downside and upside risks as possible. A useful technique is to divide the session into two phases. The first phase consists of the generation of ideas where participants put forward ideas but no discussion is permitted (except for clarification) and the ideas are listed on a flip-chart by the facilitator. The second phase of the session consists of constructive discussion of the listed ideas to identify those that deserve to be explored further, and to consider some initial thoughts on responses to the identified risks.

Cash flow: the amount of money expended on or received from a project in a particular period. The net cash flow in a period is the amount received less the amount expended in the period, and can be either positive or negative.

Discount rate: the rate of interest which is used to discount cash flows arising in the future to their present-day value. It is necessary to do this because, with positive interest rates, a sum of money which is invested will increase in value over time. Hence, the present value of money is less than its value in the future. The size of the discount rate will affect the appraised viability of those projects to which it is applied: broadly, the higher the discount rate, the lower will be the present value of earnings (or benefits) arising in the future and the greater the negative impacts on project viability. The discount rate is determined pragmatically by the sponsor. Ideally it should take account (among other things) of the sponsor's cost of capital, the rate of inflation, interest rates and rates of return on investments throughout the economy. There is a difference between 'real' discount rates and 'nominal' discount rates. Real discount rates are used in conjunction with cash flows which are expressed in terms of present-day money values, with no allowance for price inflation. (The cash flows should, however, allow for increments in future over and above price inflation – e.g. real wage increases.) Nominal discount rates, on the other hand, are higher than real discount rates and are applied to cash flows which make specific allowance for future price inflation at an estimated rate (see also Appendix 2). Some theoretical considerations regarding the choice of an appropriate discount rate are set out in Brealey and Myers (2000). See also the section 'Choice of discount rate' on page 91 of this handbook.

Downside risk: risk which relates to unfavourable outcomes.

Expected value: a best estimate of the average outcome, the sum of all possible outcomes weighted by their probabilities (see Section 2.3 and Appendix 1).

Fuzziness: one kind of uncertainty, arising from a lack of detail or precision. For example, we may have a degree of knowledge of the likelihood or consequence of an event or scenario, but the knowledge is imprecise (See Appendix 1).

Hurdle rate of return: the minimum internal rate of return acceptable to the sponsor of a particular project.

Impact: the financial value of the effect of a risk event if it occurs (see Section 2.3 and Appendix 1).

Internal rate of return (IRR): the return which can be earned on the capital invested in the project – i.e. the discount rate which gives an NPV of zero.

Investment: the creation of real or tangible capital, for example in the construction of a building or a piece of machinery, which will generate a flow of goods and services to be consumed in the future. We also use the word 'investment' to mean the assets and business activity resulting from a specific project which has been financed by capital sums.

Investment life-cycle: the lifetime of a project from inception to ultimate termination (see Section 2.4). Often there is uncertainty about the length of time over which a project will be operating and assumptions will have to be made.

Investment model: a framework for evaluating the likely profitability of the investment (see Appendices 2, 7 and 8).

Likelihood: see Section 2.3 and Appendix 1. The chance or risk that an event will occur.

Mitigation: action either to reduce the probability of an adverse event occurring or to reduce the adverse consequences if it does occur (see Chapter 5).

Monte Carlo simulation: a method for calculating the probabilities of outcomes by simulation, running a model many times, using a computer. Appendix 2 describes a stochastic approach of this kind.

Net present value (NPV): the present value of the total net cash flows generated by a project when operational less its capital cost. It is calculated as part of the process of assessing and appraising investments and makes full allowance for differences in the timing of the cash flows. The NPV can be either positive in the case of a profitable project or negative for a loss-making project. See Appendix 2, and specimen calculations in Appendices 7 and 8.

Operating risks: those risks which may affect the ongoing financial outcome once the project has come into operation – some of these risks relate to the revenue which will be generated by the project each year, while other risks relate to the costs of operation and maintenance. The definition sometimes includes risks relating to major renewals of equipment and to the eventual disposal of the asset at the end of its life.

Optimism bias: an addition to the capital cost for appraisal purposes, based on statistical analysis of past projects, to allow for the likelihood that the cost has been under-estimated (see Section 9.7 and Appendix 12).

Overall risk: the combined effect of all the individual risks and sources of uncertainty relating to the project (see Appendix 1).

Parameter: often used in this handbook to mean the capital cost, the annual revenue, or the annual operating cost.

Payback period: the period over which the total cash flow receipts from a project equal the original capital sum invested (without discounting).

PFI: Private Finance Initiative

PPP: Public-Private Partnership

Present value: the value now of a future payment, after discounting it by a suitable discount rate to recognise that it is worth less than a payment of the same amount made now (see Appendix 2).

Probability: the chance or degree of certainty of a particular occurrence taking place during a specified time period. Independent probabilities relate to events which do not depend on other events which have occurred previously. Dependent probabilities are the probabilities of occurrence once previous specified events have occurred (see Appendix 1).

Probability distribution: a distribution which relates a range of particular outcomes to their likelihood. For example, one common probability distribution is the *normal distribution* which is shaped like the cross-section of a bell (see Appendix 1).

Project: any organised business activity where an investment is made. It most commonly refers to the work of creating and operating a physical asset, such as a bridge or a building. However, it need not involve the creation of a new physical asset at all, for example if a company launches a new product which has been manufactured by existing assets. The project extends over the whole investment life-cycle of activity, not just the initial phases while the investment is being made.

RAMP: risk analysis and management for projects.

RAMP close-down report: a report prepared by the risk process manager after the project has terminated (see Chapter 8 and Appendix 11).

RAMP process plan: a plan prepared at the outset by the risk process manager, which establishes the risk strategy and baseline. The plan is updated as the work proceeds (see Chapter 3 and Appendix 11).

Real options: further options which are opened up by a decision (see Section 5.15).

Residual risks: those risks which are not avoided, eliminated or transferred in the risk response strategy (see Section 5.14).

Response: action intended either for the mitigation of downside risks or the optimisation of upside risks (see Chapter 5).

Risk: see Section 2.3 and Appendix 1 (Defining risk).

Risk analyst: an individual whose primary task is the identification and evaluation of risks during the risk review.

Risk assessment tables: tables that may be used to allocate 'scores' to risks, to help in prioritising them (see Appendix 4).

Risk custodian: an individual who has responsibility for monitoring, controlling and minimising one or more of the project's residual downside risks, or who has responsibility for monitoring, controlling and maximising one or more of the project's residual upside risks.

Risk diary: a logbook maintained by the risk process manager which should, *inter alia,* contain a record of key events in the planning and execution of the RAMP process, any problems encountered and unforeseen risks which arose, the results of the risk reviews and ways in which future risk reviews or the RAMP process itself could be improved (see Section 3.1 and Appendix 11).

Risk efficiency: a state achieved when the downside risks have been sufficiently mitigated and the upside risks optimised (see Sections 2.3 and 5.13, and Appendix 1).

Risk event: see Section 2.3 and Appendix 1. An event that could affect the success of the project.

Risk management: the process of managing risks identified in the risk review, using the risk response strategy and the risk response plan (see Chapter 7).

Risk matrix: the presentation of information about risks in a matrix format, enabling each risk to be presented as the cell of a matrix whose rows are usually the stages in the investment life-cycle and whose columns are different causes of risk . A risk matrix is useful as a checklist of different types of risk which might arise over the life of a project but it must always be supplemented by other ways of discovering risks (see Appendix 3 for a

specimen risk matrix, and the checklists on pages 87 and 106).

Risk process manager: the manager who will plan, lead and co-ordinate the RAMP process (see Section 2.10).

Risk register: a list of risks identified in the risk review process, including full descriptive detail and cross-references (see Chapter 4 and Appendix 11).

Risk response plan: a plan (prepared towards the end of the risk review) for controlling the risks once implementation begins (see Chapter 6 and Appendix II).

Risk response strategy: an overall plan for responding to the risks in the investment activity (see Chapter 5 and Appendix 11).

Risk review: an overall assessment of the risks involved in a project, their magnitude and their optimal management. Risk reviews can in principle be held at any stage in the life of a project, with each review building on the results of previous ones. Each risk review should be preceded by a risk review plan. Risk reviews should generate information for inclusion in the risk register, risk response strategy and risk response plan. The results of a risk review should be set out in a risk review report (see Chapters 4, 5 and 6 and Appendix 11).

Risk tolerance: the amount of downside risk which is acceptable to the sponsor (who will have regard also to the amount of risk or uncertainty which is acceptable to other stakeholders in the project). The sponsor's risk tolerance will often be higher in cases where the consequences of a poor outcome from the project would be small relative to the scale of the sponsor's overall business activities or resources. In devising responses to risk, the sponsor should seek to maximise risk efficiency within an acceptable level of risk tolerance.

Robustness: a system that is robust is not vulnerable – i.e. the consequences of possible damage are not out of proportion to the magnitude of that damage. For example, minor damage to a bridge by a car should not cause the bridge to collapse totally.

Scenario: a hypothetical sequence of events in the future. Scenario analysis is a process in which certain key scenarios are selected for detailed analysis, where each is thought to be reasonably representative of a *group* of real-life scenarios. One way of doing this is to select a key scenario which is thought to be near the mid-point of the group. Skill is required in defining groups which are not too large but are not so small as to require large numbers of key scenarios to be worked on. Remember that more extreme scenarios could arise in practice than the key scenarios selected for analysis. In addition those scenarios which would involve a disastrous outcome should receive special attention, even if they are thought to have only a small chance of occurring. See page 38.

Secondary risks: risks which arise from actions taken to respond to other risks (including extensions to the original scope of the project). Secondary risks can sometimes be important and always need to be analysed in their own right.

Sensitivity analysis: a technique used to discover how sensitive the results from investment models and other financial models are to changes in the input values of the variables used to calculate the results. A high degree of sensitivity is a warning to interpret the results of the model with care and circumspection, especially because many of the

input variables will themselves have been estimated and therefore be subject to error. Use of such models must not obscure awareness of their limitations and possible pitfalls, especially when they are being used for forecasting.

Sponsor: the entity which is taking overall responsibility for the project.

Stakeholders: those parties whose interests are affected by decisions about the construction or operation of an asset which they do not necessarily own or enjoy property rights in. Stakeholder interests in a local factory would include (as well as the owner) the local community, workers, investors, bank, consumers etc., all of whom are liable to be affected by decisions made concerning the construction or operation of the factory.

Stochastic model: a model using probabilities, usually involving Monte Carlo simulation.

Strategic risk: see Appendix 1. A risk which may have a major effect on the project's success.

Trend schedules: schedules which are used during the implementation of the project to record factors which could change the future risk profile of a project (see Section 7.2 and Appendix 11).

Uncertainty: incomplete knowledge of the future. All uncertainty has to be judged subjectively, in the light of one's own prior knowledge and experience, and different people may perceive different degrees of uncertainty about a given project, even if they have the same information about it. See the following sections in Appendix 1: *Uncertainty, Unforeseen and unknown risks, Mitigation of unquantified downside risks.*

Unknown risks: unidentified sources of risk which may affect the project's outcomes, but in ways which cannot currently be assessed as being either better or worse than expected.

Upside risk: risk which relates to favourable outcomes.

Variability: the expected pattern of variation in the value of a parameter, or in the occurrence of an event or scenario, or in the consequences if it occurs, considered to be measurable with sufficient accuracy in practice by a definable probability distribution, so that it is possible to predict the likelihood of a specified range of outcomes (see Appendix 1).

Vulnerability: a property of a system where small damage can cause disproportionate consequences. For example, the Ronan Point high-rise block of flats in London in 1968 was a vulnerable structure because a small domestic gas explosion in one apartment caused the whole side of the building to collapse.

Weighted-average cost of capital: the net average cost of a company's capital, after allowing for tax relief on the part which consists of debt capital.

Yield: see 'Internal rate of return'.

References and selective bibliography

(**Note**: there is an additional bibliography in Appendix 12.)

Adams, J. *Risk*. UCL Press, London, 1995.

Association for Project Management. *Project Risk Analysis and Management Guide*. APM Publishing, 2004.

Association of Corporate Treasurers. *Cost of Capital*. 1997, 2 volumes.

Berny, J. and Townsend, P.R.F. Macrosimulation of Project Risks – a Practical Way Forward. *International Journal of Project Management*, **11** (4), 201-208, 1993.

Blockley, D.I. and Godfrey, P.S. *Doing it Differently; Systems for Rethinking Construction*. Thomas Telford, London, 2000.

Boyce, T. *Commercial Risk Management*. Thorogood, London, 1995.

Brealey, R.A. and Myers, S.C. *Principles of Corporate Finance*, Irwin McGraw-Hill, 6th ed., 2000.

Cabinet Office. *Risk: Improving government's capability to handle risk and uncertainty*. Strategy Unit Report. November 2002.

Central Unit on Procurement. *No. 41: Managing Risk and Contingency for Works Projects*. HM Treasury,1993.

Central Unit on Procurement. *No. 43: Project Evaluation*. HM Treasury, 1993.

Chapman, C.B. and Ward, S.C. *Project Risk Management: Process, Techniques and Insights*. J Wiley, Chichester, 2nd ed., 2003.

Chapman, C.B. and Ward, S.C. *Managing Project Risk and Uncertainty: A Constructively Simple Approach to Decision Making*. J Wiley, Chichester, 2002.

Chicken, J.C. *Managing Risks and Decisions in Major Projects*. Chapman and Hall, London, 1994.

Confederation of British Industry. *Realistic returns: how do manufacturers assess new investment?* CBI, 1994.

Corrie, R.K. *Project Evaluation*. Thomas Telford, London, 1992.

Edwards, L. *Practical Risk Management in the Construction Industry*. Thomas Telford, London, 1995.

Engineering Council. *Guidelines on Risk Issues*. London, 1993.

Flanagan, R. and Norman, G. *Risk Management and Construction*. Blackwell Scientific, Oxford, 1993.

Godfrey, P.S. Benefiting from Risk. *Structural Engineer,* **80** (8), 2002.

Godfrey, P.S. *Control of Risk: A Guide to the Systematic Management of Risk from Construction*. CIRIA, London, 1995.

Grey, S. *Practical Risk Assessment for Project Management*. J Wiley, Chichester, 1995.

Hillson, D. *Effective Opportunity Management for Projects*. Marcel Dekker, 2004.

Hillson, D.A. Toward a risk maturity model. *International Journal of Project and Business Risk Management* **1** (1), 35-45, 1997.

HM Treasury. *Appraisal and Evaluation in Central Government*, 2003 ('the Green Book').

HM Treasury. *PFI: Meeting the Investment Challenge*, 2003, (regarding the Private Finance Initiative).

James, M. (ed.). *Risk Management in Civil, Mechanical and Structural Engineering*. Conference Proceedings, Thomas Telford, London, 1995.

Kahkonen, K. and Artto, K.A. *Managing Risks in Projects*. E. and F.N. Spon, London, 1997.

Lewin, C.G. *et al*. Capital Projects. *British Actuarial Journal,* **1** (2), 155-249, 1995

Lewin, C.G. A Case Study. *Private Finance Journal*, **1** (1), 48-56, 1996.

McGrath, R.G. Falling forward: real options reasoning and entrepreneurial failure. *Academy of Management Review*, **24** (1), 13-30, 1999.

Moder, J.J. and Philips, C.R. *Project Management with CPM and PERT*. Van Nostrand, New York, 1970.

Mott MacDonald. *Review of Large Public Procurement in the UK*. Report prepared for HM Treasury, July 2002.

Project Management Institute. *A Guide to the Project Management Body of Knowledge*, 2000 edition. Project Management Institute, Newtown Square PA, 2000.

Raferty, J. *Risk Analysis in Project Management*. E. and F.N. Spon, London, 1994.

Ren, H. Risk Lifecycle and Risk Relationships on Construction Projects. *International Journal of Project Management*, **12** (2), 68-74, 1994.

Royal Society. *Risk – Analysis, Perception and Management*. Report of a Royal Society Study Group, London, 1992.

Sadgrove, K. *The Complete Guide to Business Risk Management,* second edition. Gower Publishing Limited, Aldershot, Hampshire, 2005.

Savvides, S. Risk Analysis in Investment Appraisal. *Project Appraisal*, **9** (1) , 1994.

Songer, A.D. *et al*. Risk Analysis for Revenue Dependent Infrastructure Projects. *Construction Management and Economics*, **15** (4), 377-382, 1997.

Stewart, R.W. and Fortune, J. Application of Systems Thinking to the Identification, Avoidance and Prevention of Risk. *International Journal of Project Management*, **13** (5), 279-286, 1995.

Thompson, P.A. and Perry, J.G. (eds). *Engineering Construction Risks: A Guide to Project Risk Analysis and Risk Management*. Thomas Telford, London, 1992.

Uff, J. and Odams, A.M. *Risk, Management and Procurement in Construction*. Centre of Construction Law and Management, Kings College, London, 1995.

Vaughan, E.J. *Risk Management*. J. Wiley, New York, 1997.

Ward, S. and Chapman, C. Transforming project risk management into project uncertainty management. *International Journal of Project Management*, **21** (2), 97-105, 2003.

Walker, C. and Smith, A.J. (eds). *Privatised Infrastructure: the BOT Approach*. Thomas Telford, London, 1995.

Wilkie, A.D. A Stochastic Investment Model for Actuarial Use. *Transactions of the Faculty of Actuaries*, **39**, 341-403, 1986.

Wilkie, A.D. More on a Stochastic Investment Model for Actuarial Use. *British Actuarial Journal*, **1**, 777-964, 1995.

Woodward, D.G. Use of Sensitivity Analysis in Build-Own-Operate-Transfer Project Evaluation. *International Journal of Project Management*, **13** (4), 239-246, 1995.

Appendix 1: The meaning of risk

In order to understand and apply the RAMP process, it is necessary to understand the basic concepts associated with risk and some of the techniques used in its analysis.

Simple example

Suppose we wish to construct a bird table for the garden in the hope that it will enable us to see many birds from our window.

Baseline plans

First we prepare an outline design, and compile a budget and plan for its construction and installation. Then we consider the risks which could affect the cost and timing of the project, or our enjoyment of the results when the bird table is in use. This will involve identifying and analysing the risks, and then minimising their adverse effects.

Identifying risks

Risks can have outcomes which are more or less favourable than expected (referred to as 'upside' and 'downside' risks respectively). In the case of the bird table, examples of downside risks include:

- suitable timber difficult to obtain
- costs more than expected
- takes too long
- construction proves very difficult
- is struck by lightning after erection
- birds hate it!
- timber soon rots
- tool breaks
- concrete below soil prevents erection
- neighbours complain about the birds
- new legislation prohibits bird tables
- something else goes wrong.

There are also such upside risks as:

- materials cost much less than expected
- takes less time than anticipated
- lasts far longer than thought likely
- attracts more bird varieties than expected
- a neighbour offers to build it
- we find one second hand.

The risks differ considerably in nature. They can arise before and during construction, or after the bird table comes into operation. Some are quite likely, others extremely unlikely. Some are uncertain, in that they are very difficult to assess. For example, the chance of new legislation might seem very unlikely at first sight but could become a real possibility in the event of disease being found to be spread by birds. Some risks are trivial in their effect, while others if they occurred would spell the end of the project. Some risks are independent, but many are dependent on others (e.g. the risk of it taking too long is dependent on, among others, the difficulty of finding suitable timber).

To analyse the risk of the project taking too long, we need to look at all underlying causes of possible delay and their chance of occurrence. Then we can decide what action we can take to minimise the risks and their effects if they arise. For example, we could reduce the chance of construction proving difficult by designing the bird table in accordance with plans in a do-it-yourself magazine. Also we could buy two types of nails in case the first type proves unsuitable for parts of the construction. This would increase the cost slightly, and we would have to consider whether it is worthwhile.

Evaluating risks

We have talked about the 'chance' or 'likelihood' of

various things happening. What do we mean by this? Consider the chance of the hammer breaking during construction of our bird table. One approach would be to estimate the proportion of occasions on which the hammer had broken on other jobs. We would not have exact records but might be able to say that, based on past experience, the chance is between one in a hundred and one in two hundred. Or, not having made a bird table before, we might perceive the chance to be somewhat increased, say, to one in 50, because we shall be using longer nails than normal. But suppose the hammer was weakened on the last job without our knowing; then the shaft may break next time it is used, so that the real chance may be as high as, say, one in two.

Faced with the possibility of neighbours objecting, we might visit them to discuss our plans in advance, to ascertain their attitudes and discover how they are likely to react. This, and the previous example, illustrate that additional knowledge can dramatically alter our perception of the risks we are facing. The cost of investigating the true risks can often be worthwhile in terms of giving confidence that the project's objectives can be met.

If we were in the business of constructing and selling bird tables, then we could build up records of risks based on our experience over a large number of units. For example, if we had sold a million and 100 had been struck by lightning over a five-year period, then we could calculate that the chance of this risk event is one in 10 000. We could thus evaluate the likely cost of offering to replace them free of charge. However, if one is constructing only one bird table, does it really matter what the risk is of a lightning strike? It probably will not happen anyway. The answer depends on how seriously we view the loss of our bird table. If we regard this prospect as disastrous, it may be worth paying a small insurance premium to cover the potential loss. If the consequences of

the loss are regarded as trivial, we would probably be content to bear the risk ourselves without insurance.

Many more risks will no doubt be considered in practice, even for this simple project, before the first steps are taken. For a major project, there would be many hundreds, or even thousands, of individual risks to be considered.

Unforeseen events

However much effort is put into risk analysis, there is sometimes a totally unexpected event which can scupper our well-laid plans. In our example we completed and installed the bird table successfully. The birds liked it and flocked to it. But after a week we noticed the birds being attacked by sparrow hawks as they fed and this continued. As a result the bird table brought us no pleasure so it has now been taken out of commission.

This illustrates that in practice it is often the unanticipated risks which can destroy even a major project or render it obsolete or unprofitable. Identification and study of the *catastrophic* risks can often be the most worthwhile aspect to concentrate on, especially near the beginning of the project appraisal process. By catastrophic risks, we mean those risk events which could have very serious or catastrophic consequences, even if the probability of occurrence is thought at first sight to be low. The iceberg risk for the *Titanic* is an obvious example.

RAMP is a process which helps to identify, analyse and respond to the risks and then bring them under proper control. It puts all these different considerations into a logical framework so that they can be treated methodically without so much likelihood of important aspects being missed.

The concepts and issues illustrated by the above example are explained more fully in the following sections.

Defining risk

The word 'risk' can have a number of different meanings. Consider for example, the following statements:

- there is a risk of rain today
- there is an 80% risk of rain today
- there is a risk of getting wet if it rains today
- there is a real risk to motorists from the weather which is forecast for today.

Each of these statements is using 'risk' in a different sense. Risk is commonly used as a synonym for 'hazard', 'danger' or 'threat' – i.e. an undesirable event. It can also refer to the likelihood of an event occurring. A third meaning is the loss, injury or other outcome resulting from an event. Yet another usage is to describe the generality of volatility and uncertainty – the combined effect of all the individual risks in an investment or situation (i.e. the overall 'riskiness').

The 'R' in RAMP stands for the word 'risk' in the latter sense, meaning the potential impact of all the threats (and opportunities) which can affect the achievement of the objectives for an investment. RAMP analyses and responds to the uncertainty relating to the objectives – for both favourable and unfavourable effects. Thus, unlike the usual dictionary definition of 'risk' (which refers only to undesirable events), the RAMP interpretation of risk includes both downside and upside variations in the values involved (e.g. capital and operating costs, revenues, net present values, etc.).

In analysing risks we are contemplating future events, the outcomes of which are therefore uncertain. We cannot generally predict with absolute confidence a particular outcome. Nevertheless, using relevant experience and judgement, we can usually define the range of possible outcomes, and then derive estimates of the likelihood and consequences of each, with a reasonable degree of confidence. This is the basis of risk analysis.

In their 1992 study the Royal Society used the word 'hazard' to mean a situation having the potential for human injury, damage to property, damage to the environment, or economic loss. They reserved the word 'risk' to mean a combination of the probability, or frequency, of occurrence of a defined hazard and the magnitude of the consequences of the occurrence. However, we have found it necessary to use the word 'risk' in the wider senses referred to above, in line with common parlance.

Key elements

There are six main concepts associated with evaluating risk.

- *Overall risk:* the combined effect of all individual risks or sources of uncertainty in a situation. It can be divided into two portions: overall upside risk and overall downside risk.
- *Risk event:* a possible occurrence which could affect (positively or negatively) the achievement of the objectives for the investment.
- *Likelihood:* the chance (or probability) of the risk event occurring within a defined time period.
- *Impact:* the value of the effect of the risk event on one or more objectives if it occurs.
- *Expected value:* a best estimate of the average outcome, i.e. all possible outcomes weighted by their probabilities.
- *Risk efficiency:* a state achieved when the downside risks have been sufficiently mitigated and the upside risks have been optimised.

We shall explain each of these in turn, in the context of their use in RAMP.

Overall risk

Overall risk is the combined effect of all individual risks or sources of uncertainty in a situation, both upside and downside. We commonly say that a project is 'risky' if there is expected to be considerable downside variation or volatility in the eventual possible outcomes, or 'safe' if there is expected to be little significant downside variation. One way of measuring overall risk is to express all the possible outcomes in monetary terms, allowing for time, so as to have a common and meaningful unit of measurement. In this handbook we suggest doing this by calculating the NPV of the various possible outcomes, thus obtaining a distribution of NPVs around the NPV for the base case, showing the likelihood of achieving each NPV. This distribution is a measure of the overall risk and gives an indication of whether the project is 'risky' or 'safe', as well as an indication of the value of the possible upside and downside outcomes. (To keep the work within reasonable bounds we would not usually calculate the NPV for every single possible outcome but instead approximate by using scenario analysis or stochastic modelling.)

Of course we should not necessarily prefer a 'safe' project to a 'risky' project. Even though the 'safe' project may have less downside risk, it may also have less upside risk. Much may depend on how risk tolerant the sponsor is. If the sponsor has a high risk tolerance for a project of this size, and can accept the possibility of a large negative NPV, he may prefer the 'risky' project if it has a relatively high 'expected' NPV or if it has the possibility of a large positive NPV in some scenarios.

Risk event

Risk events are the specific happenings that can influence the success of the investment, which therefore need to be identified, evaluated and responded to as part of the risk analysis and management process. Examples are:

- delay in tunnelling for a new underground railway due to unforeseen ground conditions
- overspend caused by increased cost of land acquisition
- intervention by regulator to limit price increases
- introduction of new statutory maximum noise levels
- more use than expected.

Each risk event can be triggered by one or more causes and can result in one or several outcomes. For the first three of the above examples, these could be as shown in Table 3.

As illustrated in Fig.6, there is a likelihood that each cause will lead to the event, and a further likelihood that if the event does occur it will result in each of the outcomes. Of course, several causes can arise together, increasing the chance of the event, and several outcomes can result from the event (e.g. a delay is usually associated with an extra cost).

Causes	Risk events	Possible outcomes
Unforeseen geological conditions Man-made obstructions Site flooding	Delay in tunnelling	Late completion Less time for installation of track and equipment Increased capital cost
Higher property prices More land required Unexpected need for decontamination	Increased cost of land	Overspend on capital budget Need to reduce scope
Reduced total investment Recent price rises Appeals from customers	Regulator limits prices	More customers Lower or higher revenue

Table 3. Risk events and possible outcomes

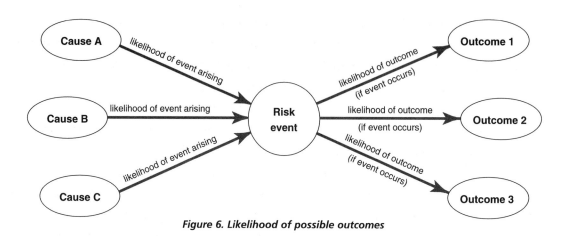

Figure 6. Likelihood of possible outcomes

Likelihood

Likelihood (or probability) is the degree of certainty that a risk event will occur during a specified time period. Typically it is measured on a scale of 0 to 100% (as in 'there is an 80% chance of rain today') or, more usually, as a probability on a scale of 0 to 1, in which 0 represents an impossible event, 1 a certainty, and 0.5 an evens chance of occurring.

The theory of probability was originally developed for games of chance, such as tossing coins, drawing cards and spinning roulette wheels. For such cases, probabilities can be calculated easily by analysis. For example, when an unbiased coin is spun there are only two possible occurrences (ignoring the unlikely event of the coin landing on its edge) – a head or a tail. There is thus an evens chance that a toss will result in a head – i.e. the probability is 1/2. Likewise, the probability of getting a black King or Queen when a card is drawn at random from a pack of 52 is 4/52 or 1/13. In each case, the probability of a particular outcome is calculated as the number of occurrences which give rise to that outcome, divided by the exposure (i.e. number of possible occurrences).

This applies provided all occurrences are equally likely and mutually exclusive (i.e. no two occurrences can happen simultaneously). Such calculations can be confirmed by experience. For example, if a coin is tossed a large number of times, say 500, the proportion of *heads* is likely to be approximately 50% of the total – i.e. about 250. Of course, for real life events the estimation of probabilities is less clear cut, but similar principles can be applied. Generally, the best approach is to use observed frequencies, from experience of similar events, if appropriate information can be obtained. If not, subjective probabilities should be used instead.

As an example, suppose we wish to estimate the probability that a new toll bridge spanning a river estuary will have to be closed due to high winds (in excess of 60 mile/h) on the day of the Royal Opening scheduled for 1 November. By consulting meteorological records kept at a weather station near the site of the bridge, we see that during the 20-day period around that date (i.e. from 10 days before to 10 days after mid-day on 1 November), over the last 10 years that records have been kept, there have been 17 days when winds have been stronger than 60 mile/h. Hence the probability of the bridge being closed because of winds is 17/(10 x 20) or 17/200, i.e. about a 1 in 12 chance.

A crucial factor in deriving measures of probability is the validity of the assumptions which need to be made. So these must be carefully checked for realism, noted and monitored. If they change, the probabilities will need to be revised. An illustration of the probabilities and underlying assumptions for the above risk events is set out in Table 4.

Impact

As defined above, the impact of an event is the value of the effect of the risk event, if it occurs, on one or more of the financial parameters of the investment – e.g. on capital cost, revenue or operating cost. Thus impacts are derived by assessing the consequences of the outcomes of an event in terms of their financial consequences for the objectives. The impact can often be expressed as the NPV of the cash flows resulting from the outcomes. Table 5 gives some examples.

Expected value

Any potential risk may or may not occur in a particular investment. In order to get a good idea of what we might reasonably expect to be the overall impact of any category of risks for an investment, we need some simple measure. That is given by the 'expected value', which is calculated by multiplying impacts by the associated probabilities of events. It is equivalent to the average impact of the risk event, which would result if we were to carry out a large number of identical projects.

Thus, for example, if the chance that a cricket ground will become unsuitable for a test match is 10% and the impact on revenue if the game is cancelled is estimated as £2 million, then the expected value of cancellation is 10% of £2 million, that is £200 000. More generally, where there are several alternative possible scenarios, the overall expected value of the variations from the base case is the sum of the corresponding expected values for each separate scenario. Let us illustrate this by returning to our test match. If the match takes place and all available seats are occupied, the gross revenues will be £3 million. There will be fixed expenses of £400 000 irrespective of seat occupancy or whether the match takes place. The base case, or most likely outcome (with a 40% probability), is that the match takes place with two-thirds of the available seats occupied. The forecast net revenue is thus 2/3 x £3 million, less £400 000, i.e. £1 600 000. If, however, the game is cancelled (which has a 10% probability), the net revenue will be £2 million worse than the base case – i.e. minus £400 000. If the match takes place but only one-third of the seats are

Risk event	Probability	Assumptions
Head on toss of coin	1/2	Unbiased coin Properly tossed Does not end on edge
Black King or Queen on draw of card	1/13	Selected at random Normal pack of 52 cards
Toll bridge being closed at Royal Opening (in above example)	17/200 = 0.085	Closure enforced if 60 mile/h winds at any time in day Wind limit does not change Weather system unchanged over last 10 years

Table 4. Probabilities and assumptions for specific risk events

Risk events	Outcomes	Impact (NPV): £ million
Ground subsidence due to tunnelling for underpass	Damage to 6 buildings	Cost of compensation 2.0
New competitor enters market for bus service	Loss of passengers	Reduced revenue 3.7
Major contractor is bankrupt	Extra cost and delay for re-tendering	Increased capital cost 1.0 Loss of early revenue 1.5

Table 5. Examples of impact of risk events (if they occur) expressed as the NPV of the resulting variations in cash flows

occupied (which has a 30% probability), the net revenue will be £1 million worse than the base case – i.e. £600 000. If there is a very favourable outcome and all the seats are occupied (which has a 20% probability), the net revenue will be £1 million better than the base case – i.e. £2 600 000.

Thus, as well as the base case, there are three alternative scenarios being considered, namely that the match is cancelled, or that only one-third of the seats are occupied, or that all the seats are occupied. We can calculate the expected value of the variation from the base case under each scenario as illustrated in Table 6.

Thus the overall expected value of the risk scenarios is minus £300 000. To obtain the expected value of the net revenue from the match, we must deduct £300 000 from the base case forecast of £1 600 000, to leave £1 300 000.

Risk efficiency

This is a key objective for any risk management process. It is achieved when we reach the point, in devising responses to both downside risks and opportunities, beyond which we believe that the marginal cost of introducing an additional response would exceed the utility to the sponsor of the resulting risk reduction or opportunity increase. The process will usually involve trial and error, to find the right set of risk responses.

To be satisfied that risk efficiency has been achieved, we need to be able to answer positively the following four questions:

- Have we exhausted all the opportunities to reduce downside risk or increase upside risk without significantly increasing expected cost?

- Have we sufficiently explored those possible responses to risk which would involve extra cost?

- Have we considered possible responses to risk which would reduce expected cost without increasing downside risk or reducing upside risk to an unacceptable extent?

- Would the marginal cost of an additional risk response, including the time and effort in searching for it, exceed the marginal increase in the sponsor's utility from the resulting risk reduction or opportunity increase, considering each possible additional risk response in turn and allowing for secondary risks?

Achieving risk efficiency will tend to determine which set of risk response actions should be adopted in practice. However, the project may still not proceed if it is not financially viable or if there is too much residual downside risk or uncertainty to meet the sponsor's risk tolerance.

Probability distributions

The expected value of £1 300 000 can be regarded as the average net revenue which would be obtained from each test match if a large number of matches were to be played. If only one match was due to be played, however, it would in addition be useful to look at the probabilities of occurrence of each of the possible outcomes, including the base case, as in Table 7: this shows the probability distribution of the net revenue. It demonstrates that there is a 10% risk of losing £400 000 and this possible outcome needs to be taken into account by the sponsor before deciding whether to proceed or

Scenario	Probability	Impact	Expected value of variation from base case
Game cancelled	10%	–£2 000 000	–£200 000
Only one-third of seats occupied	30%	–£1 000 000	–£300 000
Seats fully occupied	20%	+£1 000 000	+£200 000
	60%		–£300 000

Table 6. A test match – the calculation of expected values of three scenarios different from the base case

Scenario	Net revenue	Probability
Game cancelled	−£400 000	10%
Only one-third of seats occupied	+£600 000	30%
Base case (two-thirds occupied)	+£1 600 000	40%
Seats fully occupied	+£2 600 000	20%
		100%

Table 7. A test match – probability distribution of net revenue

not. Also, the sponsor will want to take account of the 20% chance of gaining as much as £2 600 000.

Let us take as another example a specialist developer of high-quality houses. He has found from experience that, at current prices, he can sell the following proportions of his standard 'classic' houses at each price (to the nearest £100 000):

- 0.3 at £600 000
- 0.5 at £700 000
- 0.2 at £800 000.

This can be plotted as a probability distribution and as a cumulative probability distribution, as shown in Figs 7 and 8. The cumulative probability distribution shows the probability of selling at a particular price or less. Hence the chance of being able to sell at up to £750 000 is 0.3 + 0.5 = 0.8.

Thus, from the cumulative probability distribution,

we can estimate that there is approximately a 50% chance that the selling price of a house will reach £690 000. In this example, this is the same as the expected value which is given by: £[(6 × 0.3) + (7 × 0.5) + (8 × 0.2)] × 100 000, i.e. £690 000.

Wherever practicable, recorded data is used to derive probability distributions, with adjustments if necessary to allow for future trends. However, there are many cases where this is not feasible. In such cases, if the risks involved are such as to justify quantifying, then it is necessary to estimate the probability using judgement – ideally exercised by someone with expertise in the particular area concerned.

For example, we may wish to elicit from an art expert the probability distribution for the price likely to be realised at auction for a masterpiece owned by a charity of which we are patrons. We may ask the expert to

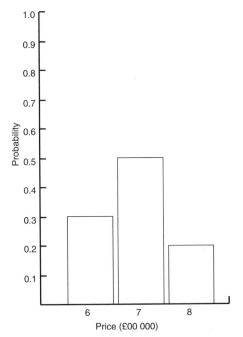

Figure 7. Probability distribution

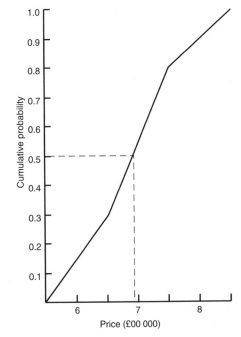

Figure 8. Cumulative probability distribution

proceed as follows (for simplicity, ignoring here the possibility that the painting may remain unsold):

- Estimate the high-impact scenario (H) which has, say, a likelihood of 10% of being reached. For the painting assume this is £400 000.
- Next determine the low-impact scenario (L) for which there is only a 10% chance (say) of it not being exceeded. Let us presume this is set at £200 000 in our example.
- Then choose either one or two intermediate points – either one-half or one-third of the distance between L and H. We assume here one at £300 000.
- Decide on a class interval – usually this can be conveniently set equal to (H − L)/2 or (H − L)/3 depending on whether there are one or two intermediate points between L and H. For the picture, the class interval will be £100 000.
- Then (using expert judgement) assign estimated probabilities (ideally rounded to one significant figure) to each class in the range. These give for the masterpiece the following distribution (to the nearest £100 000):
  - 0.3 at £200 000
  - 0.5 at £300 000
  - 0.2 at £400 000

The above discussion may seem to imply that any risk event has a single clearly defined impact if it occurs. However, in practice there is often a range of possible outcomes for an individual risk event, each of which has a different probability (i.e. there is a probability distribution for the risk). Furthermore, for each outcome of the risk event, there can be a range of impact values, each with its own likelihood of occurrence.

Chapman and Ward (2003) use a similar 'minimalist' approach. If, however, the expert thinks this approach is too crude because he has more information about the 'shape' of the probability distribution, the method can be modified as necessary.

Combining risks

A primary aim of RAMP is to evaluate and manage risks affecting the overall investment. It is therefore essential to be able to aggregate a number of risks which could potentially affect each of the investment objectives. In order to do this, we need to quantify at least the most significant risks, understand the nature of their relationships, if any, and then combine the probabilities so as to determine their collective effect.

There are two main rules for combining individual risks – probability 'addition' and 'multiplication'. These will be explained by assuming there are two events, A and B respectively, for which the probabilities of their occurring can be denoted as Prob(A) and Prob(B).

The 'addition' rule states

**Prob(A or B or both) =
Prob(A) + Prob(B) − Prob(A and B).**

The reason for subtracting Prob(A and B) is that Prob(A) includes the possibility that A and B occur together and so does Prob(B), so one Prob(A and B) is subtracted from the sum to eliminate double counting.

If events A and B are mutually exclusive, i.e. cannot occur together, then Prob(A and B) = 0, so Prob(A or B or both) becomes Prob(A) + Prob(B).

The 'multiplication' rule states

**Prob(A and B) =
Prob(A) x Prob(B), provided A and B are independent.**

By 'independent' we mean that the occurrence of one event does not influence the likelihood of the other. If, as often is the case, the events are not independent, then the multiplication rule becomes:

- If B is dependent on A – i.e. the fact that A has occurred could affect the likelihood of B's occurrence, then

**Prob(A and B) =
Prob(A) x Prob(B, given that A has occurred).**

| Scenario | Selling price of | | Probability | Total revenues: *£00 000 |
	1st home: £00 000	2nd home: £00 000		
A	6	6	0.3 x 0.3 = 0.09	12
B	6	7	0.3 x 0.5 = 0.15	13
C	6	8	0.3 x 0.2 = 0.06	14
D	7	6	0.5 x 0.3 = 0.15	13
E	7	7	0.5 x 0.5 = 0.25	14
F	7	8	0.5 x 0.2 = 0.10	15
G	8	6	0.2 x 0.3 = 0.06	14
H	8	7	0.2 x 0.5 = 0.10	15
I	8	8	0.2 x 0.2 = 0.04	16
			1.00	* + or − £100 000

Table 8. First estimate of probability distribution (assuming independence)

- If A is dependent on B – i.e. the fact that B has occurred could affect the likelihood of A's occurrence, then

Prob(A and B) =

Prob(B) x Prob(A, given that B has occurred).

Prob(B, given that A has occurred) and Prob(A, given that B has occurred) are called 'conditional probabilities' and will not generally be the same as the unconditional probabilities, Prob(B) and Prob(A).

As a simple example of using the above rules, we can calculate the probability of getting an odd number or a number less than three, or both, when we throw a six-sided die as follows:

Prob('odd' or 'less than 3' or both)

= Prob('odd') + Prob('less than 3') − Prob(both)

= 3/6 + 2/6 − 3/6 x 2/6

= 4/6 = 2/3.

In this case, Prob('odd') and Prob('less than 3') are treated as being independent. The above rules can be extended to cover the combination of any number of individual risks. However, combining risks which have probability distributions for a range of values gets more complicated. To demonstrate how this can be done, let us go back to the example of the house developer above. Suppose he plans to sell two houses over the next two months

Total revenue *£00 000	Scenarios	Combined probability
12	A	0.09
13	B, D	0.30
14	C, E, G	0.37
15	F, H	0.20
16	I	0.04
* + or − £100 000		1.00

Table 9. Result of first estimate of probability distribution (assuming independence)

and wishes to estimate the probability distribution for the total resulting selling price, assuming the two sales are independent. This can be done as shown in Table 8.

We now gather together the scenarios giving the same total revenues and hence arrive at the probability distribution shown in Table 9 for the total revenue.

As stated above, this assumes that the price of the second house is independent of that for the first. In practice, risks are rarely perfectly independent.

Two kinds of dependence can be distinguished, representing positive and negative correlation between the risks. Positively correlated risks tend to increase together, whereas negatively correlated risks move in opposite directions.

Let us now suppose the price of the second

| Scenario | Selling price of | | Probability | Total revenues: *£00 000 |
	1st home: £00 000	2nd home: £00 000		
A	6	6	0.30 (0.60 + 0.40 x 0.3) = 0.216	12
B	6	7	0.30 (0.40 x 0.5) = 0.060	13
C	6	8	0.30 (0.40 x 0.2) = 0.024	14
D	7	6	0.50 (0.40 x 0.3) = 0.060	13
E	7	7	0.50 (0.60+0.40 x 0.5) = 0.400	14
F	7	8	0.50 (0.40 x 0.2) = 0.040	15
G	8	6	0.20 (0.40 x 0.3) = 0.024	14
H	8	7	0.20 (0.40 x 0.5) = 0.040	15
I	8	8	0.20 (0.60 + 0.40 x 0.2) = 0.136	16
			1.000	*+ or − £100 000

Table 10. Second estimate of probability distribution (assuming dependence)

Total revenue: *£00 000	Scenarios	Combined probability
12	A	0.216
13	B, D	0.120
14	C, E, G	0.448
15	F, H	0.080
16	I	0.136
* + or − £100 000		1.000

Table 11. Result of second estimate of probability distribution (assuming dependence)

house has a 60% chance of falling within the same price bracket as the first house (due to word getting out) and only a 40% chance of being sold entirely

independently. We would then have the situation shown in Table 10 and the resulting probability distribution as is presented in Table 11.

This is *very* different from the preceding result based on an assumption of independence, as can be seen in Figs 9 and 10.

Many users of risk analysis tend to use techniques for aggregating risks which implicitly treat the risks as if they are completely independent. This can give seriously misleading results. Chapman and Ward (2003) point out that a high degree of dependence is typically encountered – up to 80% for costs and typically 50% for time related risks. They propose

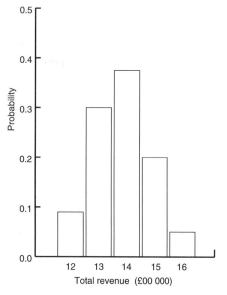

Figure 9. First probability distribution: all sold independently

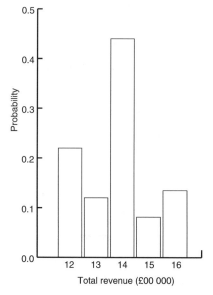

Figure 10. Second probability distribution: only 40% sold independently

Perceived risk distribution		Real risk distribution	
Value of outcome	Probability	Value of outcome	Probability
6	0.2	7	0.1
7	0.4	8	0.2
8	0.3	9	0.4
9	0.1	10	0.2
		11	0.1

Table 12. Perceived and real risk distributions

calculating the cumulative probability distributions for each of the risks being combined and then deriving a weighted average cumulative distribution to represent the combination of the risks, using as weights, r and $r - 1$ to multiply the dependent and independent distributions, where r is the correlation coefficient. The coefficient can be based on calculation or judgement.

Real and perceived risks

Perhaps the most tantalising thing about risk analysis is that, in most situations, we do not, and cannot, know the real risks that we face. Even after exposure to the risk has taken place (whether the risk event occurred or not), we still do not know what the true risks really were. Specifically, we do not know what the real risk distribution is and what will be the specific outcome for a particular risk event if it occurs. Clearly, there is a difference between perceived risk and real risk. The former is what we estimate, the latter is the true risk which currently exists. See Table 12 for an example of possible differences between a perceived and a real risk distribution.

The average values of these risk distributions are 7.3 and 9 respectively, and let us assume that the actual outcome is a value of 7. The risk distribution histograms and the actual outcome, on common axes, are shown in Fig. 11.

When and if the risk occurs we know, of course, that it lies within the real risk distribution, but not where nor what the shape of the real distribution is. In this example, the perceived risk distribution is

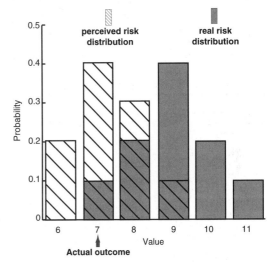

Figure 11. The outcome of the risk distributions shown in Table 12

significantly different from the real one. Yet, when the actual result turns out to be 7 – approximately equal to the estimated average value – it may be presumed, quite wrongly, that the perceived distribution was close to the truth.

Even if we had correctly estimated the risk distribution initially, it is distinctly possible that the distribution may have changed significantly before the risk exposure ends. That is why we need to be diligent in recording and monitoring the assumptions which underlie our estimates of risks, and why we need to reassess risks at regular intervals during the life of an investment.

The degree of difference between perceived and real risks depends on our level of knowledge about the risks and the situation in which they exist. We can sometimes improve our knowledge of the risks by carrying out further research in an endeavour to make our perception of the risks more closely match reality.

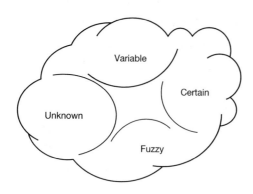

Figure 12. A person's perception of the future

Our success in estimating risks will depend on:

- availability of valid data from experience
- our level of expertise in the area of risk
- our insight into the underlying causes and factors influencing the outcomes
- the extent to which the risks are stable or subject to change
- reliability of assumptions.

In view of such difficulties, it may be asked 'Why bother?' The answer is that the risks are real and will not disappear, and so they cannot be ignored. Even if our attempts to measure risk are not entirely successful (and it is extremely difficult to measure our degree of precision), there is clearly enormous potential benefit in analysing and managing risk to the extent that is practicable. The precise probability of occurrence and the precise outcomes may be unimportant when it comes to responding to the risks, for example. Despite the difficulties of

measurement, experience suggests that, properly executed, risk analysis and management is the crucial factor in successfully carrying through any investment.

Uncertainty

'Uncertainty' means incomplete knowledge of the future. All uncertainty has to be judged subjectively, and different people may perceive different degrees of uncertainty about a given project, even if they have the same set of information about it.

As shown in Fig. 12, there are three main levels of certainty (or uncertainty).

- 'Certain' – those things we think we know for certain, for example that our project has planning permission. But even this 'certain' knowledge may occasionally be wrong – for example, if a hidden procedural defect will invalidate our planning permission.
- Partially known, of which there are two categories:
  – variable: where there is uncertainty about whether an event or scenario will occur or not, or the degree of occurrence, but it is expected to follow a discernible pattern of variation – for example, a definable probability distribution – so it is possible to predict the likelihood of a specified range of outcomes;
  – fuzzy: where there is a degree of knowledge of the likelihood or consequence of an event or situation but it is imprecise, though the approximate knowledge may be sufficient for the purpose of managing the risks involved.
- Unknown – where there is no knowledge.

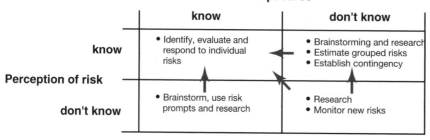

Figure 13. Degree of awareness regarding risk exposure

In practice, many known risks are fuzzy but it is assumed for the purpose of analysis that they are variable, and numerical values considered plausible are assigned to the probability distribution and the consequences of particular events occurring. For important risks the effect of using different numerical values should be evaluated (i.e. sensitivity testing).

Examples of uncertain knowledge

Uncertainty may include:

- doubts on whether there may be outcomes which are currently not foreseen as possible

- a lack of sufficient knowledge about the likelihood of foreseeable outcomes occurring and/or the consequences if they occur, even if estimates have been made for the purpose of assessing variability

- an unidentified or not properly understood mode of failure

- insufficient understanding of the extent to which the risks are dependent on other risks

- not enough knowledge about possible chain reactions, where an apparently insignificant event could, if it occurred in conjunction with other events, trigger significant consequences

- issues arising from hidden or ill-defined assumptions

- insufficient clarity in the definition of the project's objectives and success criteria or in the basic project plan

- doubts about the possibility of error or bias in the risk analysis and/or the investment appraisal

- worries about the future stability of the relationships between the numerous people and organisations involved in the project, or about possible misconceptions by some of them;

- the possibility of step changes in the 'state of the world' or in the financial, political, social, physical or economic environment surrounding the project.

A lack of recognition of incompleteness of knowledge can be a major cause of project failure,

since risk which is unrecognised usually cannot be managed as effectively as perceived risk or identified lack of knowledge. Some uncertainties may be perceived as areas where there is insufficient knowledge, while other uncertainties may not be clearly perceived at all. In some risk areas there may be relatively minor uncertainty or 'fuzziness' but nevertheless there may be thought to be a sufficiently accurate perception of the risks for many practical purposes – though an element of uncertainty about the truth of this perception will always remain.

Managing uncertainty

Uncertainty may be managed to some extent, even if it is not possible or appropriate to measure it. The management of uncertainty must always be given serious attention. A gradual process may be used, considering each area of uncertainty in turn, with a view to obtaining increased knowledge and understanding of that area and controlling the possible consequences, to the extent that it is considered feasible and worth doing so:

- Consult other knowledgeable people in a range of disciplines, who may be able to reduce or even eliminate some of your uncertainty from their own experience or knowledge.

- Carry out desk research on the events which have occurred for similar projects in the past, at home and abroad, to identify risks not hitherto perceived or to get a better understanding of the probabilities and likelihoods of various risks.

- Carry out small-scale experiments to get more precision about the risks, their likelihood and their consequences (as, for example, in drilling boreholes on a site intended for development).

- Make a desk study of the extent to which key risks may be more, or less, dependent on each other than previously realised, looking for possible underlying causes of risk.

- Carry out a brainstorming session on how adverse chain reactions might develop and what preventative action might be taken or specific early warning systems of developing chain reactions might be established.

- Make a rigorous search for hidden assumptions, additional to those already shown on the assumptions list, so that sensitivity analysis on them can be carried out.

- Look for possible ambiguities or incompleteness in the project's objectives and success criteria, or in the basic project plan, and seek clarification from the sponsor.

- Adopt a solution or approach that reduces the vulnerability to lack of knowledge and has greater robustness.

- In addition to the in-house risk analysis and investment appraisal, obtain an independent risk analysis and investment appraisal from a recognised consultant, with the aim of:
  – eliminating possible errors in figures and methodology
  – reducing bias, both deliberate and accidental
  – obtaining additional information or ideas based on the consultant's own knowledge and experience
  – ensuring the use of 'state of the art' methodology.

- For the areas of uncertainty which remain, carry out a sensitivity analysis in the investment appraisal, covering the likely range of outcomes, insofar as it can be assessed. Subjective judgements (by a knowledgeable person or group of people) may be necessary about the boundaries of this range and on the likelihood that various points within the range will be reached.

- Ensure as far as practicable that the responsibilities of the various parties are well defined, without ambiguities, gaps or overlaps. Test their understanding of their responsibilities. Check that they have allocated sufficient resources to carry out their responsibilities effectively and in a timely manner, and that they are incentivised to do so. Establish a good system of communication between the parties, so that they are all aware of progress

and new developments as the project proceeds, and make arrangements for the parties to meet periodically. Ensure that there is a good system for dealing promptly with the future public relations aspects in a way which is acceptable to all parties.

- As the project proceeds, conduct regular reviews to identify any new risks or areas of uncertainty that may have emerged and to respond to any changes in project objectives, assumptions or risks.

- Establish a crisis committee with wide powers and the ability to act quickly if a crisis or a major opportunity occurs or, just as important, if there are signs that a crisis or a major opportunity is developing (and ensure that appropriate early warning systems exist, with a sufficiently wide horizon-scanning capability to identify emerging risks and uncertainties at the earliest possible stage).

Such steps will not eliminate uncertainty entirely but, taken in combination, they may reduce it to an acceptable level and generate additional risk responses which increase the chance of project success. If, however, the remaining uncertainties are judged too great, with the sensitivity analysis showing too many situations with significant negative outcomes, then the project may have to be abandoned. Much may depend on the sponsor's level of risk tolerance for a project of this size, which in turn will depend on the utility to the sponsor of various positive or negative outcomes.

Some additional aspects of uncertainty and ways of responding to it are contained in the sections *Unforeseen and unknown risks* and *Mitigation of unquantified downside risks*. In discussing uncertainty it may sometimes be appropriate to make use of 'fuzzy' statements, where we do not have enough information to make precise or detailed statements. Fuzzy statements are discussed by Blockley and Godfrey (2000). These are high-level statements which can prevent too early a commitment to a specific idea which closes off potentially beneficial options.

Unforeseen and unknown risks

One thing is certain: for any major investment, it is unlikely to be possible to identify all of the risks which could arise. In virtually every project, problems and opportunities occur which were not anticipated. Sometimes these can have a substantial impact on an investment – e.g. the tunnel collapse in constructing the Heathrow Express, which led to doubts about the NATM (New Austrian Tunnelling Method) way of tunnelling and caused a substantial delay to the Jubilee Line Project. Clearly it is important to attempt to identify as many risks as possible in advance, to be ever vigilant to spot new risks as they emerge, and to have quick and effective responses for dealing with risk events which do arise. Unexpected downside risks typically arise due to causes in the following categories, which therefore provide a valuable checklist to help prompt our attempts to identify such risks:

- new laws, regulations or court judgments
- reactions of hostile interests
- freaks of nature
- physical environment proving unexpectedly harsh
- unforeseen man-made hazards
- new technologies
- malignant action by third parties
- project rejected for environmental or historical reasons
- unexpected financial, economic, social or political circumstances
- unexpected problems arising from design of physical assets
- unlikely accidents
- risks which could have been foreseen but were not
- breach of contract by investors, contractors, etc.
- failures of suppliers
- fraud and crime
- inadequate organisation.

There is also the point that the risk event itself may have been foreseen, but the impact may prove unexpectedly disastrous.

Recognising that, at any time, we can be only partially aware of the totality of risks to which an investment is exposed, it can be useful to have the following model of our degree of awareness regarding real risk exposures.

As Fig. 13 indicates, there are four categories of risks, namely risks which we

- know we know (i.e. K/K risks)
- know we don't know (i.e. K/DK risks)
- don't know we know (i.e. DK/K risks)
- don't know we don't know (i.e. DK/DK risks).

Commenting on each of these categories in turn

- *K/K risks:* identify, evaluate and respond to these risks using the RAMP process
- *DK/K risks:* conduct brainstorming sessions, use risk prompts (e.g. risk map, risk matrix, check lists and case studies), and undertake research to suggest possible risks which then are in the K/K category
- *K/DK risks:* if not possible or practicable to identify and evaluate individual risks, then *either* estimate grouped risks (e.g. may make overall allowance for unspecified 'design' risks or 'commercial' risks) *or* allow for risks in a general contingency budget
- *DK/DK risks:* undertake research to identify risks and monitor emerging risks – which then are in category K/K, if they can be evaluated individually, or category K/DK, if they are better treated as part of a risk group or a general contingency allowance.

Blockley and Godfrey (2000), describe a simple diagrammatic technique ('the Italian flag') which enables a group of experts confronting a particular issue to share with each other the extent to which each of them feels uncertain about possible alternative courses of action. Once the area of uncertainty has been more closely defined, this may point towards the research which needs to be done before the group can have sufficient confidence to recommend the best way forward.

Mitigation of unquantified downside risks

How can one decide how much expense it is worth incurring on a particular risk management action, if one does not know the probability of occurrence of the event one is protecting oneself against? For example, is it worth designing a bridge to be slightly wider than is necessary at present, at significant extra cost, in order to have a better chance of coping with the risk of wider vehicles or a statutory requirement for wider traffic lanes?

Such questions are perhaps best approached by looking first of all at the financial impact if the risk event were to occur, in this case probably little short of catastrophic, particularly if it happens near the start of the period of operation. Giving due weight to the consequences if the event were to happen at different points of time, let us take the average impact as £A. Suppose that the capital cost of the extra work is £B, where B is much less than A. Then, from a strictly mathematical viewpoint, if the chance of the risk event occurring during the project's life is greater than B/A, the extra work is worth doing. Thus we do not need to know exactly what the probability is, only that it is greater than B/A. It then becomes a question of judgement as to whether the probability is within this range or not.

However, this method of calculation would only be appropriate for a sponsor to whom a chance of B/A of losing £A is equal in value to the certainty of incurring a cost of £B. For some sponsors, particularly if the finances of the project are large in relation to the sponsor's own finances, the amount it may be worth spending to avoid a catastrophic

loss would be increased.

One particular kind of uncertainty is the extent to which the project may be delayed (or even aborted or cancelled) because of the influence of other interested parties who may be hostile to the project or to certain aspects of it. The best way of tackling this is to list these parties in a methodical way and assess carefully, looking from their viewpoint, what the perceived impact of the project is likely to be and their likely courses of action. For example, environmentalists might be concerned that the project is intrusive, destroys views and causes pollution: they can be expected to lobby vigorously in Parliament and perhaps take direct action once construction starts.

In some cases, it may be difficult to forecast the extent of a project's environmental impact. Whereas in the past this might have been left to chance, it will nowadays usually be essential that all aspects be studied in depth – e.g. visual intrusion, use of energy and scarce materials, pollution, noise, destruction of natural environment, effect on nearby amenities, archaeological remains, ease of eventual removal, effect on wildlife.

Such an analysis may suggest courses of action which could keep risk and opposition to a minimum. For example, environmentalists might be invited to participate in the design process, so as to highlight opportunities for reducing the adverse environmental effects. It may even be possible to improve certain aspects of the present environment by slight modifications to the project. Even if it does not prove practicable to go some way to meeting the wishes of environmentalists, the exercise will at the very least give advance warning of the principal grounds on which they are likely to object, so that relevant research can be carried out in advance.

Estimating small probabilities

How can one estimate the probability of occurrence of an extremely unlikely event? If a large number of similar projects have been carried out in the past, past experience is perhaps the best guide. Getting sufficient reliable data of what happened to all those projects might be a significant practical problem, however. If, for example, out of 10 000 bridges, five have collapsed during the past 120 years, the chance of collapse of any new bridge at some point during an assumed life of 120 years can be assessed (other things being equal) as 1 in 2000. In this kind of analysis it is important, however, to get a true correspondence between the number of cases where an event occurs and the number of cases exposed to risk of the event. If the population of 10 000 bridges included some very old ones, and only old bridges had collapsed, the chance of a new bridge collapsing within the next 120 years might be much less than 1 in 2000. On the other hand, if all the five collapses were of relatively new suspension bridges, of which 1000 had been built, then the chance of early collapse of a new suspension bridge now being built could be as high as 1 in 200.

In practice sufficient information on past experience may often not be available, and the assessment of a probability as 'very small' may be little more than informed guesswork. In such cases there is a danger that the value of the probability may be significantly mis-stated, for example a probability assessed as 1 in 1000 may actually be 1 in 100. If the event in question would have major consequences, if it occurred, it is important to deal with the uncertainty about the probability. Sensitivity analysis is one way to do so. The range of probabilities to be tested may have to be determined subjectively but needs to be sufficiently wide. The use of subjective probabilities ensures that the choices made are consistent with the beliefs of those in a position to judge how likely various outcomes are. Using subjective probabilities is always better than avoiding the issue of using probabilities because of inadequate data (see Chapman and Ward, 2002 and 2003, on processes using subjective probabilities).

Differing attitudes to risk

Even if we know precisely what the risk of occurrence of an adverse event will be, and its consequences if it occurs, it is likely that different sponsors might well have different views on whether they are prepared to accept such a risk. For example, a wealthy sponsor might be prepared to take a 10% risk of incurring a significant loss on a project, whereas another sponsor, who has lower financial resources, might not. The latter might prefer to have a lower 'expected' return but with more certainty of avoiding a loss. For this reason some sponsors will have a greater desire than others to insure against the risk of loss. Usually a risk will be worth insuring against (or minimising in some other way) if the occurrence of the risk event would cause real difficulty to the sponsoring company or its backers. If the sponsor feels that the consequences of occurrence of the risk event would be comparatively unimportant for him, he will be happy to absorb the risk without having to pay an insurer a profit margin.

Similarly most equity investors, for whom the investment is a small portion of a large portfolio, will be quite happy to accept a downside risk, provided there is sufficient upside potential. They would not normally wish to see costly risk-mitigation action taken if this reduced the 'expected' net present value of the project. For such an investor the losses on some projects are more than balanced out by the gains on others.

Banks which have lent money, on the other hand, cannot usually benefit from the upside potential of a project and their main concern is to avoid downside risks occurring to such an extent that the loan cannot be repaid. They will often be wanting as much risk mitigation to take place as is reasonably practicable, unless there is external security for the loan.

Appendix 2: Using an investment model

To evaluate any investment, it is necessary to define its objectives, measure these (as far as possible) in financial terms, and then relate the resulting financial parameters to some overall measure of value for the investment over its life (typically whole-life net present value, as explained below). Generally, the value of an investment is based on the balance of benefits over costs. Typically the main measures of cost and benefit, stage-by-stage, are shown in Table 13.

Benefits and costs are both typically spread over periods of time, as cash flows. It is impossible to conduct anything other than the simplest investment appraisal without building a cash flow model.

Appraisal techniques

There are a number of techniques currently used to appraise projects, which are all based on the principle of comparing costs with benefits. Most appraisals are conducted using either a payback period, IRR or NPV. The latter is perhaps the most widely used approach, with good reason.

The payback period is simply the number of years of cash flow needed to meet the initial investment. Its simplicity has, however, to be offset by lack of consideration of the time value of money and of cash flows and risks beyond the payback period. The second method, IRR, does not have these disadvantages but gives no indication of the amount of value or profit each project will provide. The NPV approach overcomes these difficulties, although it does introduce subjectivity in the requirement to establish a discount rate.

Real or nominal cashflows

Investment appraisals are generally conducted initially on the basis of real costs and revenues, calculated in terms of today's money value. Using nominal cash flows, allowing for future inflation,

Stage	Description	Key financial parameters		Other parameters*
		Benefits	Costs	
1.	Opportunity identification		Cost of study	
2.	Appraisal		Appraisal cost	
3.	Investment planning		Financing cost	
4.	Asset creation		Capital cost	Scope Performance/quality Timing
5.	Operation	Revenue Non-revenue benefits	Operating cost Maintenance cost Renewals cost	
6.	Close-down	Resale/residual value	Decommissioning cost Cost of staff redundancies Disposal cost	
* These have potential impact on one or more financial parameters				

Table 13. Measures of cost and benefit

could be confusing at this initial stage because it would produce absolute figures which, particularly in the later years, might be extremely large and hold little relevance in today's terms for such an appraisal. However, adjustments must be made to allow for any costs and benefits which will not escalate approximately in line with future inflation, and these adjustments may need to be based on assumptions about future inflation rates.

Where the project is going to be financially free standing, normally financial models will also be required at a later stage which are based on nominal figures allowing for an assumed rate of inflation in calculating future cash flows. Sensitivity testing using different assumed inflation rates will usually be necessary, in view of the uncertainty in this field. These financial models will also need to allow for any fixed rate funding and the effect of taxation on the economics of the project. Consolidation of accounting statements will also require nominal figures.

It may sometimes happen that a project that appears financially viable using real costs and revenues looks unprofitable once the full financial model is prepared, and *vice versa*. Even if (as we would recommend) the risk analysis is carried out using real costs and revenues, in order to retain a good 'feel' for all the estimates made in respect of future years, it would still be worth running a preliminary version of the full financial model at a fairly early stage, to prevent abortive work on a project which will not meet investors' financial requirements.

Choice of discount rate

The generally accepted discount rate appropriate to the analysis of UK public service investments is 3.5% per annum in real terms. Many commercial firms use discount rates higher than 3.5%, which serve to reduce the significance of future revenues, and

maintenance and operating costs, over the whole life of the asset in comparison with initial construction costs. This handbook shows how to link RAMP with an investment model but it does not purport to discuss all aspects of the construction of that investment model or the discount rate to use. In particular the choice of an appropriate discount rate is an important but complex matter which is outside the scope of this handbook. Ultimately the choice of the discount rate will depend partly on issues such as the company's cost of funds and any hurdle rates that the company sets for its investments. Some companies may wish to use a higher/lower discount rate for projects which they regard as having a higher/lower inherent risk (i.e. a risk which is incapable of mitigation) than for their other projects. If this inherent risk varies significantly over different phases of the project, it may sometimes be appropriate to use different discount rates for each phase.

A high discount rate should not be seen as a substitute for a detailed risk analysis as this could lead to the rejection of profitable low risk projects in favour of more profitable projects that carry unacceptable levels of risk (see Section 1.5). Where the cash flows are based on nominal figures, a higher discount rate will be appropriate than where real cash flows are used.

Actuaries can advise on the choice of a suitable discount rate for the purpose in hand, taking account of the above-mentioned points and developments in modern financial theory in recent years.

Discounting

Discounting is at the heart of the NPV technique. The rationale for discounting is based on the fact that a sum of money now is worth more than at a future time. For example, if we have to forego having £100 in cash for (say) 12 months, then we would need to be paid a sum of interest to cover the loss in value of the money (due to inflation) and the opportunity missed to earn some return by investing the money for a year. Thus if we judge that our losses for waiting a year are 8%, then we are saying that £100 today is equivalent in value to £108 in a year's time.

Another way of saying the same thing is that £100 in a year's time is worth

$$£(100 / (100 + 8)) \times 100 = £92.59 \text{ now.}$$

Similarly, £100 in two years' time is now worth

$$£(100 / (100 + 8)) \times (100 / (100 + 8)) \times 100$$

i.e. $£(100 / (100 + 8))^2 \times 100 = £85.73$

If interest is expressed as a fraction (i.e. 8% = 0.08) then we can restate the above, expressing the net present value of £100 in one year as $£(1 / 1.08) \times 100$ = £92.59. Extending the calculations, Table 14 can be used to calculate the NPV of a cash flow of £100 per year at the end of each of the next three years.

Thus we can express any future cash flow as a net present value by using the above formula and an appropriate interest (or 'discount') rate.

As another example, suppose the total capital cost of a project is £50 million, of which £20 million is spent at the end of year 1 and £30 million at the end of year 2. Then, at a discount rate of 10%, the NPV of the capital cost is: $£[(1/1.1) \times 20 + (1/1.1)^2 \times 30]$ million = £42.97 million.

Thus each key parameter affecting the value of an investment, whether it is an individual payment or a series of cash flows, can be expressed as an NPV. Finally, by adding the NPVs for benefits and deducting those for costs, an overall whole-life NPV for the investment can be calculated.

A deterministic or a stochastic approach

The traditional approach to projecting future cash flows, the deterministic approach, is to consider each item separately and estimate its most likely value. The next step is to conduct sensitivity tests which typically involve making a pessimistic and optimistic estimate in addition to the most likely. All of the results of the investment appraisal are then presented based on three scenarios; pessimistic, optimistic and the most likely.

The conclusion that can be drawn from such an analysis is necessarily limited. The answer may lie somewhere between the pessimistic and optimistic scenarios and is most likely to be the middle scenario. But how likely is most likely and is optimistic equally as likely as pessimistic? To answer these questions – and others such as, what is the probability of a rate of return less than x% or between y% and z% – a stochastic approach may be needed.

A stochastic approach involves fitting statistical distributions to cash flow items. Where there is only limited information about a particular risk, it may be possible to use a subjective estimate of the statistical distribution which is consistent with the information that is known and may be sufficiently accurate for practical purposes.

As a consequence of inputting data into the cash flow model in the form of statistical distributions, the result of the investment appraisal can also be presented as a statistical distribution (see example shown in Figs 14 and 15). Having a distribution of NPVs from such an appraisal clearly provides decision makers with the ability to make more informed decisions. It allows an assessment of probability of

Years	Future value: £	NPV formula	Value now: £
1	100	$(1/1.08) \times 100$	92.59
2	100	$(1/1.08)^2 \times 100$	85.73
3	100	$(1/1.08)^3 \times 100$	79.38
	NPV		**257.70**

Table 14. Net present value of a cash flow of £100 per year

Real project costs	£ million
Development costs	1.80
Land purchase	2.30
Design work	4.20
Building costs	32.50
Plant and machinery	22.50
Consultant's fees (technical, risk etc)	3.80
Pre-opening costs	4.60
Total costs (current prices)	**71.70**

Key dates	
Construction starts	July 2006
Operations start	October 2008
Major refurbishment	July 2015

Assumptions (margins over RPI)	p.a.
Revenue (£13 m. per annum initially)	-0.50%
Operating costs (£3 m. per annum initially)	0.50%
Capital costs — buildings	2.00%
— plant and machinery	1.00%

Figure 14. Typical investment model

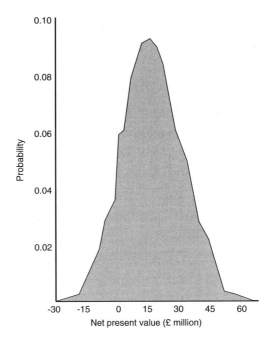

Figure 15. Net present value at 6% real discount rate

loss calculations and gives a better insight into the sensitivity of the project to adverse conditions.

This stochastic approach has to be used with discretion. Dependence should be allowed for; thus it would be inappropriate to ignore the fact that there is a linkage between short-term interest rates and inflation. The number of cash flow items expressed as a statistical distribution should also be limited in order to make the process more realistic and manageable.

The decision on whether to use a stochastic or a deterministic approach depends on the scope of the investment appraisal. Clearly, the level of sophistication required and the information that is likely to be available will determine the approach to be adopted. A stochastic approach is therefore only likely to be appropriate for medium to large projects.

Scenario analysis is a useful practical alternative to a full stochastic approach (see Section 9.2 and the section *Probability distributions* in Appendix I). It is likely to be worthwhile to carry out scenario analysis before embarking on a stochastic model, because the former is much less expensive and can often give a sufficient 'feel' of the risks for the purpose in hand. Moreover, scenario analysis helps to avoid the danger, inherent in stochastic modelling, of losing sight of the key assumptions on which the results depend.

Accuracy

Even a simple model has to be correct. The nature of cash flow models is that small mistakes can have significant consequences, particularly for marginal projects. It is essential that models are documented and independently audited, both for structure and accuracy of input. Equally important is the reasonableness of the cash flows. Clearly, they are only estimates but they should be checked by a third party where possible, and validated against past experience. Allowance must be made in the cash flows for all the 'knock on' effects arising from the project in respect of the sponsor's central costs or other activities.

Appendix 3: A RAMP risk matrix

Figure 16. An example of a RAMP risk matrix (for downside risks)

Source of risk

Column key:
- **1. Political/social** — a) Government, b) Public opinion, c) Environmental change, d) Legislation, e) Wars, terrorism, riots, f) Poor public relations, g) Crime
- **2. Business** — a) Demand failure, b) Competition, c) Premature obsolescence, d) Safety standards
- **3. Economic** — a) Cost inflation/interest rates, b) Currency fluctuations, c) Extreme economic conditions
- **4. Project** — a) Lack of definition, b) Technical innovation, c) Lack of technical competence, d) Lack of commitment, e) Lack of leadership, f) Poor planning and control, g) Inadequate legal framework, h) Inadequate resourcing of project, i) Inadequate progress on project, j) Labour relations, k) Human error or incompetence
- **5. Natural** — a) Bad weather, b) Earthquake/volcanic eruption, c) Fire or explosion, d) Adverse ground conditions
- **6. Financial** — a) Inadequate financial margins, b) Unbalanced sharing of risk

Investment stage/risk event

1. Opportunity identification
2. Appraisal — } no significant risks
3. Investment planning and preparation

Investment stage/risk event	1a	1b	1c	1d	1e	1f	1g	2a	2b	2c	2d	3a	3b	3c	4a	4b	4c	4d	4e	4f	4g	4h	4i	4j	4k	5a	5b	5c	5d	6a	6b
Promotion of concept																															
loss of intellectual property rights							x															x									
claims for infringement of intellectual property rights							x															x			x						
Design																															
non compliant design (failure to meet specified standards)															x		x		x	x									x		
design based on inadequate site investigation data															x		x		x	x									x		
professional negligence							x								x		x		x	x	x								x		
Contract negotiations																															
failure to agree development framework with sponsor															x		x		x			x								x	x
failure to resolve conflicts of interest within promoting consortium															x		x		x			x								x	x
contractual terms and conditions worse than expected																						x								x	x
Project approval																															
failure to obtain approval/consents	x	x																		x	x										
long delay before approval granted	x	x			x																		x								
unforeseen modifications to project		x													x	x						x							x		
cost of obtaining approval higher than expected	x	x			x																	x									
inclusion of contingent liabilities (e.g. environmental clean up)	x	x									x																				
introduction of regulatory controls (fares, competition policy)	x		x	x							x																				
4. Asset creation																															
Raising of capital																															
capital requirements increased by inflation												x	x	x																	
interest costs higher than expected												x	x	x																	
capital not available due to market conditions														x																	
capital not available due to poor market perceptions of project						x																								x	x
capital not available due to withdrawal of support by key organisations						x			x											x		x		x						x	x
refinancing not available or terms worse than expected						x														x		x								x	x
default due to insufficient project revenue								x		x										x										x	x
default due to external factors			x		x		x	x												x											
Construction																															
inability to obtain land, access right, wayleaves		x																													
compensation costs higher than expected	x	x			x	x																									
delays due to force majeure			x																							x	x	x	x		
delays due to other causes (e.g. unforeseen ground conditions)			x			x													x	x		x	x	x		x			x		
cost over-runs											x	x					x			x		x	x	x		x	x	x	x		
insolvency of promoter										x																				x	
insolvency of contractor										x																				x	
third party damages																				x								x			
failure of project to gain technical acceptance			x												x	x				x		x	x								
structural failure post completion							x										x		x												
5. Operation																															
Expenses and maintenance																															
unforeseen operating costs			x	x		x					x	x								x		x				x					
major repairs			x	x																x		x					x	x			
third party claims																				x		x						x	x		
accident damage																				x								x	x		
Revenue																															
operating volume less than expected			x			x		x	x	x									x			x									
unit revenues lower than expected				x				x	x										x			x									
unforeseen competition			x	x					x													x									
revenue collection costs higher than expected							x															x									
revenues negotiable (influence of large customers)									x													x									
loss of revenue due to late completion or temporary closure																				x		x				x			x		
revenue insufficient to cover debt servicing								x												x											x
revenue loss due to fraud			x				x													x											
6. Close-down																															
lifetime below expectations			x	x				x	x	x	x																x	x	x		
residual value less than expected			x										x	x																	
dismantling costs higher than expected	x		x									x								x							x	x	x		

94

Appendix 4:
Risk assessment tables

This Appendix describes a very simple technique which is designed to assist in the prioritisation of downside risks for analysis (see Section 4.3). The idea is that each risk event is first of all classified into one of several 'likelihood' categories, according to its probability of occurrence, and is then classified into one of several 'consequence' categories, according to the severity of the consequences if the risk event occurs. Each category has a score and the score for likelihood is multiplied by the score for consequence to get the combined score for the risk event. The risk events with the highest combined score are then selected for priority analysis.

Set out below are some specimen risk assessment tables. However, it should be emphasised that there is a variety of ways in which such tables can be drawn up, so as to meet the needs of the particular project, with different categories and differing decision rules about which risks should be eliminated, managed or ignored.

To explain the use of the specimen tables, suppose that a particular risk event has a 30% chance of occurring at least once during the project's life-cycle. If it occurs, it will be a serious threat to the investment. It will be awarded a score of 8 in Table 15 and a score of 100 in Table 16, leading to a combined score of 800 (see Table 17). According to the suggested decision rule, this risk event would come into the category of undesirable – i.e. a risk which one should attempt to avoid or transfer if at all possible.

Suppose, however, that the same risk event had been assessed as having a disastrous consequence if it occurs. Then the combined score would have been 8000, which means it is an intolerable risk. If it cannot be eliminated, transferred or avoided, the whole future of the project may be in doubt.

Description	Scenario	Probability	Scale value
Highly likely	Very frequent occurrence	Over 85%	16
Likely	More than evens chance	50–85%	12
Fairly likely	Quite often occurs	21–49%	8
Unlikely	Small likelihood but could well happen	1–20%	4
Very unlikely	Not expected to happen	Less than 1%	2
Extremely unlikely	Just possible but very surprising	Less than 0.01%	1

Table 15. Risk assessment table – likelihood. This table categorises risks according to their probability of occurring at least once at some point during the whole project life-cycle

Description	Scenario	Scale value
Disastrous	Business investment could not be sustained (e.g. deaths, bankruptcy)	1000
Severe	Serious threat to business or investment	100
Substantial	Reduces profit significantly	20
Marginal	Small effect on profit	3
Negligible	Trivial effect on profit	1

Table 16. Risk assessment table – consequence

Likelihood		Consequence				
		Disastrous (1000)	**Severe** (100)	**Substantial** (20)	**Marginal** (3)	**Negligible** (1)
Highly likely	(16)	16 000	1600	320	48	16
Likely	(12)	12 000	1200	240	36	12
Fairly likely	(8)	8000	800	160	24	8
Unlikely	(4)	4000	400	80	12	4
Very unlikely	(2)	2000	200	40	6	2
Extremely unlikely	(1)	1000	100	20	3	1

Table 17. Risk assessment table – acceptance of risk

Points	Category	Action required
Over 1000	Intolerable	Must eliminate or transfer risk
101–1000	Undesirable	Attempt to avoid or transfer risk
21–100	Acceptable	Retain and manage risk
Up to 20	Negligible	Can be ignored

Key to acceptance of risk

As pointed out in Section 4.3, risk assessment tables can sometimes be misleading, in that they may fail to draw attention to some of the key risks which ought to be studied and possibly eliminated, avoided or transferred. Such tables are not an essential step in the RAMP process and should be used with caution, if at all.

Appendix 5: Insuring downside risk

Introduction

While traditional insurance markets exist for specific established exposures, the insurance industry is starting to innovate successfully by devising new flexible forms of cover which meet the need for an integrated and holistic approach to the insurance of project risks. Emphasis is beginning to shift from the mechanical placement of insurance for single risks, which has hitherto been the traditional approach, to the devising of an optimal outcome for a package of risks over the lifetime of a project.

In the UK, projects coming under the Private Finance Initiative (and derivative programmes like Public-Private Partnerships) typically demand a broader and more flexible stance from insurers in tackling the umbrella of risks within a project, and insurance markets have been able to respond to this demand. As insurance markets become increasingly familiar with the type of risks covered, the scope for continued innovation to the benefit of the client will grow.

Common risk categories

While all projects are different, common categories of risk for major projects include:

- loss of assets during and after construction
- unforeseen ground conditions
- loss of income stream due to delay in construction completion
- insufficiency of revenue stream (e.g. due to erroneous forecasting)
- liability to third parties

- design liabilities
- liability to employees
- failure of information technology.

Methods of insurance

Insurance is usually arranged in relation to a particular phase of the project and the following describes some of the ways that large projects are insured.

The construction phase

Construction all risks (CAR): Insurance against physical loss or damage of assets used during construction, including the contract and temporary works, mechanical and electrical equipment, construction plant and equipment, and any existing buildings or structures to be retained.

Third party (public) liability: Indemnity if there is legal liability to third parties for physical injury or damage to property. Extension of cover to provide insurance for pure financial loss and for design faults may be possible.

Professional indemnity: Legal liability caused by negligence in carrying out 'professional' duties for third parties. This must be considered alongside the contractual structure, the liabilities of the parties within the project and third party liability insurance.

Employer's liability: An indemnity which covers the employer against legal liability if employees suffer physical injury or disease while in their employ.

Advance loss of profit: Cover if revenue from a project is interrupted because of delays caused by physical loss or damage insured under a CAR policy. Cover is provided for a range of financial losses such as debt servicing through to remuneration of full gross profits (income less cost savings). The individual exposures of all participants in the project need to be considered.

The operational phase

Material damage: Cover against loss or damage to the physical assets of the project. Areas of cover that need to be addressed include whether to insure against mechanical and electrical breakdown; whether cover should be against all risks or only for specified perils; whether cover should be 'as new' or should reflect asset depreciation.

Business interruption: Interruption to the revenue stream caused by physical loss or damage. Cover can range from the cost of servicing debt through to gross profits foregone. Cover can be extended to include denial of access, utility failure and other risks.

Latent defects: Cover for structural damage, imminent threat of collapse or failure of the weatherproofing envelope – including consequential loss – arising from a latent defect in construction which manifests itself in the first 12 years after construction.

Third party (public) liability: Legal liability to third parties for personal injury (including disease) and damage. Pure financial loss extension should be considered.

Employer's liability: Legal liability for injury to employees. The Transfer of Undertakings (Protection of Employment) Regulations should be considered in relation to questions of liability for employees of acquired businesses.

Motor: Damage to owned vehicles, or those leased or hired to the project, together with associated liability to third parties.

Directors' and officers' liability: The legal liability of directors and officers of the project arising from their managerial position.

Others – specific to the project: Depending on the circumstances of the project, other coverages, such as medical malpractice liability, key-man insurance, etc., need to be considered.

Extending the risk management strategy

Apart from obvious legislative limitations and restrictions incorporated into the process, the scope for creative solutions increases as we move away from the working layer (attritional losses), and as risks are combined and the terms extended. One of the most important aims in combining risks over a period of time would be to take a more strategic perspective on the handling of risk and achieve longer term objectives – such as the smoothing of the premium levels and the achievement of cash flow stability, as well as building long-term strategic alliances with insurers.

Another key driver to what strategy is adopted is the probable size of projects and exposures, and whether it is likely that traditional insurance markets will find it difficult to absorb the risk. Traditional insurance may exist, but at a price that is not economic. A commercial view may be needed on whether insurance represents value for the risk which is being transferred. When considering whether to insure risks that they have not previously insured, insurers are likely to be much more receptive if relevant statistics of the frequency and severity of the risks concerned are available from past experience.

Insurance markets available

As well as pre-existing insurance markets, new markets may need to be created and early involvement by insurers and risk experts in establishing these is critically important, especially if projects are very large. The availability of insurance is likely to depend on the availability of data and knowledge of the risks (and familiarity of the insurance markets with the risks). The aim is to design a customised solution package that will give the broadest cover at the most economic price possible, using an optimal combination of financial markets.

Limited risk transfer

Below are summarised a number of ways in which risk can be transferred to a limited extent, which can be useful where full insurance cover cannot be obtained:

- *Unfunded self-insurance:* whereby the owner would simply pay losses, as and when they arise, from cash flow.

- *Pre-funded self-insurance:* in which cash is set aside for this purpose in a stable financial asset.
- *Owned captive:* a limited purpose insurance company specially formed to insure or re-insure the risks of its parent company.
- *Rent a captive:* this is a funding vehicle owned by a third party which operates as an insurance company for a limited number of participants.
- *Mutual:* an insurance company owned jointly by a group of entities, all of which have homogeneous exposures to risk, such as the partners in a consortium.
- *Post loss funding:* funding of losses by borrowing from equity or debt markets, etc.
- *Financial insurance/reinsurance products:* use of insurance policies to fund risk exposures.
- *Insurance derivative products:* the principle of these products is similar to financial derivatives.

Acknowledgement
The working party is indebted to Aon Risk Consultants for kindly supplying a paper on which this Appendix is largely based.

Appendix 6: Mitigation and control of risks in computer projects

For large computer projects the following suggestions are offered for risk mitigation:

- establish the objectives and the business case very clearly and comprehensively at the outset;

- identify the lead sponsor, if more than one sponsor is involved, and set up a clear machinery for decision-making by the sponsors;

- consider running a pilot project;

- subdivide the project into semi-independent modules;

- use established software which is already working, as far as possible (even if there is some loss of functionality), reserving any brand-new software to a relatively small part of the whole;

- avoid as far as possible any technologies which have not previously been tested thoroughly in practice;

- draw up a clear specification;

- check carefully that the project, if delivered according to specification, will fully achieve the objectives;

- ensure there is clear ownership of the project at an appropriately senior level;

- employ consultants to ensure that there is a good blend of IT expertise and business expertise and a genuine partnership between the experts on each side;

- revisit the project specification to see if further modifications can be made to reduce the risks which have been identified;

- define clearly which risks will be borne by the contractor and which by the sponsor(s), and

write the contract accordingly with an appropriately structured payment mechanism;

- take up references regarding contractors' performance on previous projects;

- choose a contractor with a record for reliable delivery, even if not lowest cost;

- give appropriate financial incentives (or penalties) to the contractor to ensure maximum effort on his part to control risks;

- set up well-defined mechanisms to control specification changes, with appropriate levels of authorisation;

- use a flexible design that can readily be adapted to cope with legislative changes, and establish an early warning system that flags adverse consequences of legislative changes in time;

- address the toughest design issues first;

- pay particular attention to the user-friendliness of any component of the system which will use the Internet;

- ensure that the development team has sufficiently high-quality 'back up cover' in case some members fall sick or leave;

- consider whether insurance could play a part (e.g. key-man insurance);

- establish contingency plans to extend the life of the current system should there be a time over-run on the new project;

- set up a system for testing in modules the parts of the system which involve new software or new technology, with contingency plans for dealing with the situation should they not work;

RISK ANALYSIS AND MANAGEMENT FOR PROJECTS

- establish contingency plans in case the contractor goes out of business while the project is being developed or under warranty;
- plan in detail the transition from the old system to the new.

Once the project is authorised, it is vital that proper machinery should be put in place to control the residual risks, including:

- appointment of a fully competent project manager with a clear remit and defined authority;
- preparation of containment and contingency plans;
- appointment of risk custodians;
- appropriate budgetary controls, including contingency allowances for minor variations;
- strict controls on even minor specification changes;
- controls to make sure that all the intended risk mitigation actions are in fact taken;
- a crisis management committee that can be called at short notice;
- establishment of project 'landmarks' at the outset, with dates attached to them – some of these landmarks will be followed by additional

gateways requiring reaffirmation of project continuance;
- a detailed procedure for monitoring and analysing trends;
- full communication to all concerned;
- regular risk reviews, including reviews of whether the project (when completed) will still meet customers' needs if these have changed;
- a project steering group, meeting monthly, to consider emerging issues of policy, timing or resource constraints, on which all interested parties should be represented, at a sufficiently senior level, and the project manager should attend.

Note: Large IT projects are often actually IT-enabled business change projects, and hence great attention needs to be paid to the robustness of the case for the business change, and the risks involved in that business change, as well as the IT-specific risks set out above. Experience has shown that, where such projects have failed, this is often due to a failure of the business change rather than a failure of the IT component.

Appendix 7: A simple RAMP appraisal process

Introduction

This Appendix presents a simple process for appraising competing projects and choosing between them, using RAMP methodology for risk assessment, combined with a suitable investment model. A practical example of the process is given, together with a method for deciding whether responding to risks is financially worthwhile or not.

Process summary

It will be assumed here that the company's weighted-average cost of capital is 6% p.a. plus price inflation. (A different rate can, of course, be used if appropriate.) The process of appraisal for each project may be summarised as follows:

(a) Determine the objective(s), scope and requirements of the project and work out the project plan, at least in outline.

(b) Carefully evaluate the cash flows each year into the future, on the basis of no inflation, assuming that the most likely scenario for the project occurs.

(c) Discount these cash flows to the present time using a discount rate of 6% p.a., to get the NPV of the project.

(d) Construct alternative scenarios and repeat steps (b) and (c) above.

(e) Attach probabilities to each scenario and hence obtain a probability distribution of the NPVs. Also weight the resulting NPVs by the probabilities to obtain a weighted-average NPV.

(f) Consider risk response and amend the probability distribution of the NPVs (and the weighted-average NPV) to allow for the risk response measures which are to be adopted.

Once the calculations have been completed, a decision can be made on which of the projects has the most attractive probability distribution of NPVs. This will not necessarily be the project with the highest expected NPV, if that project has a substantial downside risk.

We shall now consider each of the above steps in more detail.

Determination of objective(s) and plan

The first and most crucial step is to determine the objective(s) of the project. This should not be done lightly but needs careful consideration so as to make sure that all the vital objectives are captured. For example, the objectives of a new railway will not be merely to transport passengers and freight and make a profit but to do so safely. The scope and requirements of the project will need thought, including such matters as whether to build in spare capacity, the degree of flexibility required, and the safety considerations once it is operational. The next step will be to work out the project plan, at least in outline: how will it be done, how long will it take, how much business can be expected, etc?

Evaluation of cash flows

Even at a preliminary stage it is essential to evaluate the forecast cash flows properly, with as much accuracy as possible, and taking account of 'knock on' effects. Mistakes or carelessness here could lead to incorrect investment decisions. Forecasts should, where possible, be reality-checked against comparable projects. Consideration should be given to whether the effect (if any) of the project on the sponsor's tax position needs to be taken into account as a cash flow. Throughout this Appendix cash outflows will be taken as negative and cash inflows as positive. Most projects will commence with negative cash flows at the outset, as capital is invested, and will then start to receive positive cash flows once the asset being constructed has become operational.

Discounting the cash flows

A useful simplifying assumption is that cash flows take place halfway through the year to which they relate. In the initial years when capital is being invested this assumption may be wide of the mark, but the effect on the NPVs is likely to be so small that it can be ignored at the initial stages of the work. We shall discount all the cash flows to a point six months after the commencement of the investment – i.e. halfway through the first year. Hence we shall assume that the expenditure incurred in the first year of the project does not need to be discounted at all and that the revenue earned in (say) the fourth year of the project is discounted for exactly three years. (For the chosen project a more accurate discounting calculation can be made as a check before the final decision is made to go ahead.)

Consider an example of a computer software project which is expected to take one year to design and implement, and which will then result in net cost savings for four years. The cash flows for the most likely scenario are expressed in terms of present day prices (£000s) with no allowance for future inflation (Table 18):

Year	Cash flow £000s
1	– 1000
2	+ 300
3	+ 400
4	+ 400
5	+ 400
Total	+ 500

Table 18. *Cash flows for most likely scenario in terms of present day prices (£000s) with no allowance for future inflation*

NPV

$$= -1000 + 300/1.06 + 400/1.06^2 + 400/1.06^3 + 400/1.06^4$$

$$= -1000 + 283 + 356 + 336 + 317$$

$$= 292$$

Thus the project can be expected to earn a future flow of profits after allowing for the cost of capital, equivalent to a lump sum of £292 000 at the outset. This assumes, of course, that things go according to plan.

Construction of alternative scenarios

The next step is to identify and analyse the major risks in the project, paying particular attention to the underlying causes. A risk is 'major' if its consequences would be serious, even if it is unlikely to occur. Ways of identifying risk include:

- checklists of problems from previous similar investments, other case studies, technical papers, safety reviews and environmental impact studies;
- site visits;
- review of baseline plans, other key documents and outline designs;
- brainstorming sessions.

A list of commonly found risks is set out at the end of this Appendix, but this list is not exhaustive. For each risk event, the consequence if it occurs must next be identified. The results are entered up in a risk register for the project. Upside potential as well as downside risk must be identified and analysed. Any assumptions which have been made in identifying or analysing the risks should also be recorded.

Some alternative scenarios for the project will then be constructed, having regard to the risks which have been analysed. This is a matter for judgement, where one is sometimes trying to capture, in only a very small number of scenarios, a wide range of risks. A useful way of constructing a scenario is to select the mid-point of a possible range of variation. Thus, for example, if there could be a cost increase, should a specified risk event occur, of between £200 and £400, the scenario would take £300 as the mid-point. Some risks can be grouped, at least at this early stage of the analysis.

Let us assume that, for the computer project given as an example in 'Discounting the cash flows', the risk analysis leads to the identification of the following major alternative scenarios (Table 19).

Then we have the following analysis (Table 20).

Scenario	Type of risk	Risk event	Probability of occurrence	Expected impact on project
A	Expected	None	55%	None
B	Upside	As A and system know-how can be sold to other organisations	10%	Revenue £200 000 more in year 2
C	Downside	Technological delay	15%	System takes extra year and cost increased by £300 000
D	Downside	System does not work well	10%	Savings reduced by £100 000 each year
E	Downside	Technological delay and system does not work well	10%	As in scenarios C and D

Table 19. Major alternative scenarios

	Scenario				
Year	A £000	B £000	C £000	D £000	E £000
1	−1000	−1000	−1000	−1000	−1000
2	300	500	−300	200	−300
3	400	400	300	300	200
4	400	400	400	300	300
5	400	400	400	300	300
6	–	–	400	–	300
Net cash flows	500	700	200	100	−200
NPV	292	481	−64	−54	−391
Probability of occurrence	55%	10%	15%	10%	10%
Expected (weighted average) NPV = 155					

Table 20. Obtaining a probability distribution of NPVs

Hence on 65% of occasions such a project would show a profit but on 35% of occasions it would show a loss. The loss could be as high as £391 000 but might be even more, remembering that scenario E is the mid-point of a range of possible outcomes. On average a large number of such projects would show a capitalised profit (after taking account of interest costs) of £155 000 each.

Risk mitigation

Let us suppose that the external contractor who will carry out the work is prepared to bear the whole of any extra software development costs (as in scenarios C and E), provided that the contract price is increased by £80 000. Is it worthwhile for the sponsor to accept this offer?

We can evaluate the various scenarios again, assuming that this new condition applies, as in Table 21.

The project will now show a profit on 80% of occasions and a loss on only 20%. Moreover, the 'maximum' (mid-point) loss is reduced from £391 000 to £188 000. This risk profile may well be more attractive than the original one to a

sponsor who would find losses hard to bear. On the other hand, for a large sponsor where the project is one among many projects, the better expected NPV of the original situation (£155 000 instead of £145 000) would suggest that the risk should remain unmitigated.

Further work for the chosen project

The method can, of course, be adapted as necessary. A higher degree of analysis would be appropriate for a very large project, for example, and this might involve stochastic modelling once a rough 'fix' had been made by scenario analysis. Moreover, a much more careful application of RAMP methodology is desirable for the selected project (even for a project of quite a small size and cost), since this will help in:

- identifying further risk response options;
- controlling the residual risk remaining after response actions have been taken.

Particular attention should be paid to any 'disaster' risks, to see if they can be mitigated at a reasonable cost. Any assumptions, which have

	Scenario				
Year	A £000	B £000	C £000	D £000	E £000
1	−1080	−1080	−1080	−1080	−1080
2	300	500	–	200	–
3	400	400	300	300	200
4	400	400	400	300	300
5	400	400	400	300	300
6	–	–	400	–	300
Net cash flows	420	620	420	20	20
NPV	212	401	139	−134	−188
Probability of occurrence	55%	10%	15%	10%	10%
Expected (weighted average) NPV = 145					

Table 21. Evaluation of the various scenarios

been made at an earlier stage, should be rechecked to see if they are reasonable. Sensitivity testing should be undertaken, to see what would be the result of varying key assumptions. (For example, in the above-mentioned computer project, it was assumed that four years' worth of benefits would be obtained – but suppose the system became prematurely obsolete and only three years' worth of benefits were achieved before a better system came into operation? Or what would be the effect of altering the assumed probabilities of the different scenarios?)

Conclusion

The process outlined in this Appendix depends for its success on the input of good quality data and carefully calculated cash flows. It also needs the exercise of good judgement in the construction of appropriate risk scenarios. Every project has its 'champion' and it is important to avoid bias, whether intentional or unintentional, when obtaining data from such a person. Appraisals should preferably be carried out by people who can take an objective view of the various factors. Only an outline of the process can be given here, to indicate the way in which project appraisal can incorporate RAMP risk analysis in a simple and practical way. Actuaries can help firms and public bodies to draw up procedures and methods to adapt the process to their own particular needs.

SOME COMMONLY FOUND RISKS

Some of the areas where risks often exist in projects are:

Downside risks

- Insufficiently defined objectives
- Design problems
- Incorrect or biased cash flow estimates
- Suppression of key information
- Capital cost
- Usage and revenue
- Running cost
- Time taken to become operational
- Efficiency level once operational
- Premature deterioration
- Premature obsolescence
- Competition (including new players)
- Force majeure
- Fraud/crime
- Political and social developments
- New laws on environment, trade restrictions, higher taxes, etc.
- Planning permission
- Opposition from third parties
- Safety hazards
- Unproven construction methods or leading-edge technology
- Loss of key personnel
- Insolvency of contractor
- Disagreement among a group of sponsors
- Hidden, unstated or untested assumptions
- Obtaining finance
- Danger from need to refinance later
- Increased cost due to interest rate or exchange rate changes
- Decommissioning when project life is over
- Economic downturns

Upside risks

- Project scope
- Potential for improved design
- Costs, revenues, timescales
- Project life
- Financial and tax structure
- Involvement of partners

Appendix 8: Applying RAMP to a large project – a case study

Introduction

The RAMP process is to be used to support the decision to invest in and then to monitor the following (hypothetical) project. It is proposed that a tolled road bridge should be built across a river estuary which is at present served only by car ferries. Two large towns, A and B, are separated by the river. The new bridge will reduce their distance by road from the present 120 miles (using a bridge further up river) to only 20 miles. Most road traffic between A and B uses the car ferries and the overall journey time is about 60 minutes at present. This will be reduced to about 25 minutes once the new bridge has been built.

Alternative sites

There are three possible sites for the new bridge. Option 1 involves tunnelling through a hill for the access road, with consequent expense and risk. Option 2 does not involve tunnelling and is in many ways ideal, except that it would involve the destruction of a historic castle and some ancient woodlands and sites of special scientific interest. Option 3 would use a site much further down the estuary. Although this would necessitate a longer bridge, the approach roads would cross greenfield sites and the overall cost of construction would be less than under Options 1 or 2. The principal problem with Option 3 is that the site can be windy and on 20 days a year high-sided lorries would have to be banned.

Traffic forecasts

At present 5000 cars and 1000 lorries a day use the ferries. The toll is 60p per car and £3 per lorry, so the overall gross revenue for the ferry operator is £6000 per day. Both A and B are expanding rapidly and it is thought that the new bridge will stimulate further traffic growth because of the reduced journey time. The new bridge will take five years to plan and construct and it is estimated that after it has been in operation for five years (i.e. ten years from the outset) the total traffic volume on the bridge will be about 15 000 cars and 3000 lorries per day. The ferries will remain in operation but it is estimated that they will attract only one-tenth as much traffic as the bridge. The bridge is assumed to have an operating life of at least 50 years. Operating expenses are estimated at £0.8 million per annum.

Preliminary appraisal

The preliminary appraisal of the project proceeds by making some simple discounted cash flow calculations, using the present ferry tolls. These calculations suggest that the project may be viable on Options 2 and 3, but probably not viable from a financial viewpoint on Option 1 unless the tolls are raised. (See the Annex to this Appendix for illustrative calculations relating to this and subsequent stages of the appraisal.)

Preliminary risk assessment

A high-level preliminary risk analysis is made, from which it is concluded that there is a significant risk, if Option 2 is adopted, that there will be a long delay and that the bridge will probably not get planning permission because of opposition from conservationists. Therefore Option 2 is rejected.

Second risk assessment

At this point the team concerned with the project holds a brainstorming session to identify the risks involved in the remaining options. They produce the following list:

- planning consent denied
- towns A and B do not expand as fast as expected
- fire, hurricane, earthquake, terrorist activity
- more efficient ferry service introduced
- Option 1 tunnel collapses
- discovery of archaeological remains delays construction
- maintenance costs higher than expected
- capital cost overrun
- ferry company reduces prices and takes more traffic
- petrol tax is raised
- bridge collapses due to faulty design or assembly
- heavy repairs needed
- ship collides with bridge.

Desk-top analysis

Further study produces the following additional list of risks:

- tolls prohibited by new legislation
- nationalisation of bridge companies
- weather pattern changes, so bridge available for less time per year
- tolls diverted through fraud
- premature obsolescence.

Evaluation

For each of these risks a preliminary assessment is made of the probability of occurrence, the impact on the project finances, and an assessment of how the risk in question can be managed. Scenarios involving 'upside' are also considered, for example, the possibility that more traffic may use the bridge than anticipated. For each scenario (whether upwards or downwards) the financial effect on the project return is calculated, assuming that the event in question occurs.

Review stage

The project team then reviews the work which has been done to date. Ideas are generated for possible modifications to the project, in order to reduce some of the risk areas or improve the likely rate of financial return. A further brainstorming session is held, which develops the following list of possibilities:

- raise toll levels
- strengthen the bridge at extra cost
- construct a service area at one end of the bridge
- buy up the ferry company and its fixed assets
- re-examine whether there is an alternative site not previously identified
- allow advertising on or near the bridge
- build windshields to increase the availability of the bridge on windy days
- build a tunnel instead of a bridge.

A decision is now taken on whether it is worth proceeding to the later stages of the analysis.

Model building

At this stage a simple mathematical model is built, based on the experiences of similar projects elsewhere, to show the effect on costs and revenues of a number of alternative scenarios. One of the key tasks is to model the traffic flow across the bridge in the event of the ferry company offering various levels of service and charges and with the tolls for the bridge being set at alternative levels. Another task is to refine the probability estimates for the various scenarios, carrying out research where necessary on the experience of similar completed projects elsewhere. After appropriate testing the model is used to re-run the analyses referred to above with a greater level of confidence.

Planning of risk response

For each of the risk areas identified, consideration is given to possible risk response options, based on the brainstorming discussions and consideration by experts, with the results shown in Table 22.

In the light of this analysis, some preliminary investigations are made into the possibility of acquiring the ferry company and its assets. Professional advice provides an estimate of the likely price and a judgement is made (supported by the mathematical model) that the bridge toll could be at least 10% higher if the ferry tolls were controlled. Some simple discounted cash flow calculations suggest that the overall project would be financially viable. It is therefore decided that the project will now have two principal activities – building and operating the bridge and also buying the ferry company, with a view to controlling its activities and tolls.

Table 22. Risk response options

Risk	Likelihood	Impact	Chosen action
Planning consent denied	low	very high	discuss with planners at early stage
Towns A and B do not expand at expected rate	low	high	none
Fire, hurricane, earthquake or terrorist activity	low	high	insure
More efficient ferry service	low	high	buy ferry company
Tunnel collapses	low	high	use proven methods and quality contractors
Discovery of archaeological remains	low	medium	add contingency plan and budget
Higher maintenance costs than expected	high	low	none
Capital cost overrun	high	low	obtain fixed price contract
Ferry company reduces prices to take more traffic	medium	high	buy ferry company
Petrol tax imposed, resulting in reduced traffic	low	low	none
Bridge collapses	low	very high	impose quality regime, and incentivise designers and contractors
Heavy repairs needed	low	medium	impose quality regime, and incentivise designers and contractors
Ship collides with bridge	low	medium	work with harbour authority and design for high visibility
Tolls prohibited by new legislation	low	very high	none
Nationalisation of bridge company	low	high	none
Weather more severe, limits availability	low	medium	insure
Tolls diverted through fraud	medium	medium	insure with fidelity bonds/improve financial management
Premature obsolescence	low	medium	design-in maximum flexibility

Third risk assessment

A further brainstorming session is held to identify the additional risk areas from the proposed ferry company acquisition, with the following results:

- acquisition proves more costly than anticipated
- acquisition proves impossible after substantial costs incurred
- Government rules that resulting monopoly of crossing would be unacceptable
- ferry company has hidden liabilities – e.g. for quay maintenance
- ferry company pension fund proves to have a deficit
- competing hovercraft service introduced by a third party
- unexpectedly heavy capital expenditure on ferries required in next five years before bridge opens
- ferry staff strike in protest at bridge plans
- ferry disaster results in lawsuits
- new EU regulations increase costs of ferry operations.

Further risk mitigation exercise

Each of the additional downside risk areas is considered in depth, with a view to identifying how the risk can be mitigated or eliminated. This is an important step (analogous to the consideration given to possible response options in the Table 22 on page 109). The conclusion is reached that the additional risks can be mitigated sufficiently and that the scope of the project does not need to be enlarged further.

Finance

The next stage is to consider how the project might be financed. Since there remain a number of risks where no action can be taken to manage them, the project will need to be financed at least partly by investors who are

prepared to absorb these risks – e.g. equity shareholders. On the other hand part of the necessary finance might well be obtainable from banks and bondholders, if they judge that the residual risks, after the mitigation actions outlined above, are sufficiently low as not to be likely to jeopardise the interest payments and the eventual repayment of the sum lent. Discussions need to take place with the merchant banks who will be aware of the terms which prospective investors and lenders are likely to accept. The RAMP report itself may be a useful document for the purpose of demonstrating to investors and lenders the following critical points:

- that the risks have been properly identified and evaluated
- that the downside risks have been mitigated as far as possible
- that the residual risks are clearly identified and quantified, and will be well managed.

Preparation of the submission

A formal RAMP report is prepared, describing in some detail the results obtained from the analysis. This is accompanied by a recommendation for the decision-makers on whether to proceed and, if so, whether Option 1 or Option 3 should be adopted. The report also

- identifies the key risks and shows how it is planned to respond to at least some of them
- presents a discounted cash flow calculation showing the expected financial outcome and the extent to which this is likely to vary in practice - some sophisticated computer-based simulations of possible outcomes, and their likely probabilities, may lie behind this calculation
- identifies how the project is to be financed and the degree of commitment which has been obtained
- describes how the project will be monitored and controlled during the construction period and the initial operation.

Decision

For a major project like this the decision-makers will need to understand the project, and its risks and rewards, intimately. Not only will they read the submission very carefully but they will talk to members of the project team and as many of the key players as possible, such as leaders of the local community, politicians, civil servants etc. They may wish to obtain an independent view on the project from an external consultant. They will certainly wish to consider carefully any scenarios which could have a severe adverse effect on the project's financial outcome, even where the probability of such scenarios occurring is considered small. Finally the decision-makers will bring to bear their own experience, intuition and judgement, paying special regard to any relevant environmental, social or political considerations, and any known bias among the members of the project team.

The interests of any groups adversely affected by the project will need to be weighed carefully in the balance. A decision will be needed on which of the alternative options for the project should be adopted. A competent project management team will need to be appointed.

Monitoring arrangements

Detailed plans for controlling the remaining risks will be drawn up and approved. Appropriate monitoring arrangements will be established, with formal RAMP reviews planned to be carried out at intervals or when major unexpected developments occur. The key risk areas envisaged will have been identified at the outset but the effect on the project's viability of any changes in the level of risk should be considered carefully. The periodic reviews should also consider other risk areas which may have come to light subsequently. The computer-based simulations will need to be updated and revisions to the financial projections prepared. A major purpose of the reviews will be to identify options for improving the eventual financial outcome or reducing the downside risks still further in the light of new developments. Particular attention will be paid to whether 'milestone events' identified in the risk response plan have been achieved to time, and to the outlook for the achievement of future milestones. The results of the reviews, and recommendations on any major decisions required, will be communicated to the senior decision-making level.

Conclusion

The main points that this case study illustrates are summarised in Section 9.2.

Annex: The investment model

This Annex gives an indication of how the NPV calculations would proceed for the above bridge case study. However, the work is taken only to a very elementary level, to illustrate the principles involved. It will be assumed that the NPVs are calculated at a discount rate of 6% p.a. and that tax is ignored.

The assumed cash flows are shown in Table 23 (on a 'most likely' basis) for each of the three options identified in the case study.

The cash flows shown in Table 23 and their NPVs are summarised in Table 24.

Sensitivity calculations are then performed based on:
- slightly optimistic values, i.e.
  — revenues 10% higher
  — operating costs 25% lower
  — capital costs 5% lower
- most likely values
- slightly pessimistic values, i.e.
  — revenues 10% lower
  — operating costs 25% higher
  — capital costs 5% higher

The results are illustrated in Table 25.

The results suggest that the project may be profitable but that the risks involved could produce a loss.

Phase	Year	Option 1: £ million	Option 2: £ million	Option 3: £ million
Planning and construction	1	−10.0	−8.0	−8.0
	2	−15.0	−14.0	−13.0
	3	−15.0	−14.0	−13.0
	4	−20.0	−16.0	−16.0
	5	−8.0	−10.0	−8.0
Operation	6	2.0	2.0	1.8
	7	2.8	2.8	2.6
	8	3.6	3.6	3.4
	9	4.5	4.5	4.3
	10	5.4	5.4	5.2
	11–55 (p.a.)	5.8	5.8	5.6
Termination	56	−20.0	−20.0	−20.0

Table 23. Assumed cash flows for the three options of the case study

Note: The figures for the operating life in years 6–55 have been obtained by deducting the assumed operating expenses (£0.8 million p.a.) from the gross revenues.

	Option 1		Option 2		Option 3	
	Total: £ million	NPV: £ million	Total: £ million	NPV: £ million	Total: £ million	NPV: £ million
Total capital	−68.00	−57.19	−62.00	−51.90	−58.00	−48.69
Total operating expenses	−40.00	−9.42	−40.00	−9.42	−40.00	−9.42
Total gross receipts	+319.30	+70.68	+319.30	+70.68	+309.30	+68.33
Termination costs	−20.00	−0.77	−20.00	−0.77	−20.00	−0.77
		+3.30		+8.59		+9.45

Table 24. Summary of the cash flows for the three options of the case study

	NPV		
	Option 1: £ million	Option 2: £ million	Option 3: £ million
Slightly optimistic	15.59	20.62	21.07
Most likely	3.30	8.59	9.45
Slightly pessimistic	−8.99	−3.44	−2.17

Table 25. Results of sensitivity analysis

The scenario method of analysing risks, for Option 3 only, is illustrated in Table 26. The sub-scenarios in Table 26 may be combined into 12 scenarios, as shown in Table 27.

The weighted average NPV is £7.20 million. It will be seen that the NPV is negative – i.e. the project would make a loss – under scenarios 4, 7 and 10, although there is less than a 5% probability of this occurring.

There is a 0.5% probability that the bridge will be destroyed prematurely in its lifetime (for one of a variety of reasons). If this occurs in, say, 27 years' time, the NPV of the loss of net revenue is about £15.6 million, which would cause nearly all the scenarios in Table 27 to show a loss.

The following package of risk response measures has been proposed:

- Let a fixed-price construction contract for payments having an NPV of £50 million.
- Insure against the risk of destruction by paying a premium of £30 000 p.a. If destruction occurs, the policy will pay a sum equal to the discounted capital value of all future net revenue.
- Purchase the ferry company for £5.5 million; it is assumed to have positive cash flows over the next ten years which have an NPV of £5.0 million at 6%, so there is a 'loss' of £0.5 million of NPV.

The first measure above eliminates C_1 and C_2. The second eliminates the destruction risk. The third is assumed to replace the bridge revenues sub-scenarios by those shown in Table 28.

If this risk response package were implemented, we would have the four new main scenarios shown in Table 29.

The weighted average NPV is £10.88 million. This distribution of NPVs is better than that shown by Table 27, since the weighted average has increased and negative values have been eliminated. It is still a matter for judgement as to whether the project is now acceptable, however, since the possibility of errors of estimation must be taken into account, as well as any risks which have not been specifically evaluated.

	Sub-scenarios	Range: £ million	Mid-point: £ million	Probability	NPV: £ million
Capital costs	C_1	57–59	58	0.8	−48.69
	C_2	59–67	63	0.2	−52.89
Operating costs p.a.	O_1	0.7–0.9	0.8	0.7	−9.42
	O_2	0.9–1.5	1.2	0.3	−14.13
Revenues p.a.*	R_1	5.0–6.2	5.6	0.1	59.79
	R_2	6.2–6.6	6.4	0.8	68.33
	R_3	6.6–7.8	7.2	0.1	76.87

Table 26. Results of scenario analysis (Option 3)

* The figures quoted are for years 11–55; the figures for years 6–10 are assumed to be adjusted *pro rata*. Note: Sub-scenarios C_1, O_1 and R_2 correspond to the 'most likely' NPVs. Sub-scenario C_2 relates to the risk that construction is delayed or becomes more expensive for a variety of reasons, including a rise in the price of labour and raw materials. Sub-scenario O_2 envisages that wage rates may rise and more operatives be required. Sub-scenario R_1 relates to the risk that tolls may have to be reduced if the ferry company reduces its tolls. Sub-scenario R_3 relates to the possibility that tolls will not be constrained to present levels, either because the ferry company raises its own tolls or because the bridge proves able to charge a premium rate.

Scenario	Sub-scenario	Probability	NPV: £ million
1	$C_1O_1R_1$	0.056	0.91
2	$C_1O_1R_2$	0.448	9.45
3	$C_1O_1R_3$	0.056	17.99
4	$C_1O_2R_1$	0.024	−3.80
5	$C_1O_2R_2$	0.192	4.74
6	$C_1O_2R_3$	0.024	13.28
7	$C_2O_1R_1$	0.014	−3.29
8	$C_2O_1R_2$	0.112	5.25
9	$C_2O_1R_3$	0.014	13.79
10	$C_2O_2R_1$	0.006	−8.00
11	$C_2O_2R_2$	0.048	0.54
12	$C_2O_2R_3$	0.006	9.08
		1.000	

Table 27. Sub-scenarios combined into 12 main scenarios

Sub-scenario	Range: £ million	Midpoint: £ million	Probability
R_4	6.2–7.0	6.6	0.8
R_5	7.0–9.0	8.0	0.2

Table 28. Revenues after eliminating ferry competition

Scenario	Sub-scenarios	Probability	NPV:*£ million
13	O_1R_4	0.56	9.30
14	O_1R_5	0.14	24.24
15	O_2R_4	0.24	4.59
16	O_2R_5	0.06	19.53
		1.00	

Table 29. Four new main scenarios

* including the cost of risk response measures

Appendix 9: Description of the RAMP process

Overview of the RAMP process

Activity A – Process launch

A1   Organise and define RAMP strategy

A2   Establish baseline

Activity B – Risk review

B1   Plan and initiate risk review

B2   Identify risks

B3   Evaluate risks

B4   Respond to risks

B5   Assess residual risks

B6   Plan responses to residual risks

B7   Communicate strategy and plans

Activity C – Risk management

C1   Implement strategy and plans

C2   Control risks

Activity D – Process close-down

D1   Assess investment outturn

D2   Review RAMP process

Activity A – Process launch

(See Chapter 3.)

A1 Organise and define RAMP strategy

A1.1   Confirm the perspective from which the risk analysis and management is being carried out and the principal stakeholders interested in the outcome.

This version of the RAMP process assumes that risk is being considered from the viewpoint of the sponsor (i.e. the party which makes and owns the investment). The process can be adapted to suit other interests.

A1.2   Appoint the 'risk process manager', who will plan, lead and co-ordinate the risk analysis and management process, and report on its results. Define the reporting line.

A1.3   Prepare a preliminary brief on the objectives, scope and timing of the investment, including an assessment of its value and importance to the sponsoring organisation, and its complexity.

A1.4   Define and agree the provisional overall strategy for risk reviews and management throughout the investment life-cycle, including each of the following:

- purpose of RAMP
- level of risk analysis to be carried out
- scope of review
- timing of risk reviews
- budget for RAMP.

A1.5   Ensure that this strategy for RAMP is fully provided for in the investment/project master plan and communicated to all parties involved.

A1.6   Form a RAMP process team by identifying and assigning those who will act as 'risk analysts' to identify risks, help to evaluate them and devise suitable responses.

A1.7   Introduce a 'risk diary' and maintain it throughout the RAMP process.

A2 Establish baseline

A2.1   Establish the baseline by defining the context and basis for the risk analysis and management process. This involves determining the information outlined in Section 3.2.

A2.2   Set out the RAMP strategy and baseline information in the 'RAMP process plan'.

Activity B – Risk review

(See Chapters 4, 5 and 6.)

The risk reviews will be performed at crucial stages or time intervals in the investment life-cycle. The process activity for the first full review is described below. Subsequent risk reviews will revise and update the analysis and resultant actions.

B1 Plan and initiate risk review

B1.1   Review and confirm (or appoint) the risk process manager and the 'risk review team' for this review (refer to step A1.6 above).

B1.2   Decide on the purpose, scope and level of the risk review.

B1.3   Plan the review by
- compiling an action plan
- defining resource requirements
- establishing a budget and timetable.

Set out the above information, together with the aims, scope and level of analysis from B1.2, and the staffing and organisation for the risk review, in the form of a 'risk review plan'.

B1.4   Brief the RAMP review team using the risk review plan.

B1.5   Inform all of the other parties likely to be involved about the review, its purpose and timetable, and the names and roles of the people undertaking the review.

B2 Identify risks

The aims in this phase of RAMP are to
- identify, as exhaustively as practicable, all significant types and sources of upside and downside risk and uncertainty associated with each of the investment objectives and the key parameters relating to these objectives
- ascertain the causes of each risk
- assess how risks are related to other risks and how risks should be classified and grouped for evaluation.

This is clearly a crucial phase. If a risk is not identified it cannot be evaluated and managed. The process of searching for and responding to risks is iterative.

B2.1   First, each risk analyst attempts to list the risks associated with each objective, key parameter, major 'deliverable' or principal activity within that risk analyst's area of focus. Make sure that every relevant aspect of the investment is analysed by the team of risk analysts. The first attempt should be from first principles without the use of any checklist or other prompts, to avoid constraining the process of discovery. Resulting risks are listed in the 'risk register'.

B2.2   Then the risk analysts should repeat the exercise with the help of the 'risk matrix' and other prompt aids such as

- checklists of problems and opportunities from previous similar investments and projects, other case studies, technical papers, safety reviews and environmental impact studies
- site visits
- review of baseline plans, other key documents and outline designs.

List the resulting risks in the risk register for subsequent review and analysis, with a tentative indication of the significance of each risk ('clearly significant', 'possibly significant' and 'probably insignificant') and inter-relationships between risks. 'Significant' is to be interpreted as implying a risk whose potential consequence or expected value is such that it could have a significant effect on one of the objectives, parameters or 'deliverables', even if it has only a small probability of occurrence. At this point, no risks should be eliminated or ignored, because even seemingly minor risks can combine to have a major impact.

B2.3   Bring together some or all of the risk analysts, and others who can make a valuable contribution, for a brainstorming session to review the risks previously identified and to flush out further risks. The brainstorming should be in two parts: the first starting with the risks identified by the risk analysts, but without other prompts; the second attempting to find additional risk exposures with the aid of a risk matrix and any other appropriate prompt lists. Encourage participants to mention even seemingly unlikely risks and scenarios. Extend and revise the risk register in the light of the results of the brainstorming.

B2.4   It may be appropriate to interview or commission experts in particular aspects of the investment to identify risks which might otherwise be overlooked or not understood. It might also be useful to search relevant literature describing case studies of similar investments to learn about the risks they encountered, and the mitigation measures and responses adopted. Again, any resulting risks are entered in the risk register.

B2.5   Classify and if appropriate group risks to assist in their evaluation. Consider each risk in the risk register in turn to determine and record:

- possible cause or causes of the risk
- trigger events giving rise to risk occurring
- possible timing and potential frequency of occurrence
- range of possible consequences – both physical and financial
- asset component, factor or activity associated with the risk
- objective, 'deliverable' or parameter impacted
- other related risks
- form of relationship with other risks
- who currently owns the risk
- the initial responses to the risk
- whether there are any risks which should be eliminated because they duplicate or overlap with each other.

B2.6   The analysis and understanding of risk groupings and relationships is often aided by representing them in the form of precedence, influence, risk/response or other diagrams, appended to the risk register with suitable cross-references.

B2.7   Update the assumptions list established at stage A2.1. Consider whether further identification work is needed: if so, return to B2.1.

B3 Evaluate risks

B3.1   For each identified risk which is 'significant' or 'potentially significant', assess in the first instance qualitatively and approximately:

- likelihood/frequency of the risk occurring per unit of time or some other convenient unit – i.e. will it occur once in every week, month, year, ten years, 100 years, etc? (The paragraph below describes some ways of expressing likelihood.)
- potential consequence (with respect to one or more of the parameters or related cash flows)
- most likely frequency of its occurrence during the lifetime of the investment
- likely timing of its impact.

Note: risk assessment tables (see Appendix 4) may be a useful aid to prioritisation of risks, if used with caution.

The likelihood (or probability) of a risk event, assessed in the first entry in the list above, may be expressed in several ways

- once and for all chance of occurrence
- average rate of occurrence over duration of investment
- variable rate of occurrence
- physical extent of occurrence (e.g. per kilometre of rail track)
- probability of each of a series of possible values or ranges of values over the life of the investment (i.e. a probability distribution).

It is important to start with a natural/convenient basis for estimation, and link this to a life-cycle estimate. If there is a range of possible values, it may be acceptable, provided the range is not too wide, to represent the range by its mid-point or average value. If a risk is related to one or more other risks – in the sense that they share common causes, or for other reasons the occurrence of one affects the likelihood of another – the related risks should be evaluated together. If the risks are not related – i.e. are independent, they can be evaluated separately. Enter the resulting assessment of each risk or group of related risks in the risk register. Include the risk that the assumptions shown in the assumptions list may not come true.

B3.2   Review the significance of risks and reclassify them into significance categories as at stage B2.2.

B3.3   For risks which are 'probably insignificant', decide whether the risks can be ignored, covered within a general risk category or retained specifically in the analysis. Do not ignore risks unless you are absolutely confident they are trivial.

B3.4   Identify as two separate categories those risks which could have

- serious or catastrophic consequences or high expected values
- exceptionally favourable consequences.

All the risks in both categories are likely to need particular, individual attention when assessing the overall 'riskiness' of the investment.

B3.5   Decide which risks justify, and are amenable to, more detailed evaluation and quantification. Generally, these are the risks with the largest expected values or, if probabilities are low, with the most serious consequences. In choosing the risks for further analysis, ensure that the likely benefit accruing from refining the estimate is worth the effort and cost involved. However, this does not apply to risks with catastrophic consequences (even if the probability of occurrence is thought to be low) as these are nearly always worth further study.

B3.6   For each such risk, conduct a more detailed and quantified evaluation of likelihood, consequence, timing, expected value and dependencies, noting carefully any assumptions made.

B3.7   For each activity affecting each parameter of the investment, compile an estimate of the potential impact of unknown and unforeseen risks over the phases of the investment life-cycle, based on experience and the complexity and uncertainties associated with the activity and parameter. It may be appropriate to do this by identifying general categories of risks and making a contingency allowance for each, based on previous experience in similar investments. Enter the results of the evaluation in the risk register.

B3.8   Assess the overall impact of risks on each parameter affecting the investment, using a scenario analysis (or computer-based Monte Carlo simulation if appropriate), and carefully note any assumptions made.

B3.9   Using the investment model and parameter estimates, determine the overall impact of risks on the whole-life NPV of the investment.

B3.10   Conduct a sensitivity analysis, exploring the range of NPV for potential variations in the parameter values associated with each of the principal risks (including those with possibly favourable outcomes). This addresses 'second-order' risks, associated with the parameter assumptions, to assess confidence in the quantification of expected values and volatility measures. Assumptions like 'independence' can be tested in this framework, but general 'robustness' tests are difficult, and it is important to be sensitive to the impact of key assumptions.

B3.11   Make a preliminary assessment of the major risks which can be avoided, transferred or reduced in other ways (see mitigation measures in B4 below) by
- deciding provisionally – for each significant risk in the risk register – whether it could and should be avoided, reduced or accepted
- making a preliminary decision on the most appropriate form of action for risk avoidance, reduction or containment, stating multiple options where relevant, and recording in the risk register
- assessing the likely effect of the mitigating actions on the risk and its expected impact, including cost of action and bearing in mind 'secondary risks' resulting from the actions, and recording in the risk register.

Consider also the major upside risks and decide on the responses which could be adopted.

B3.12   Consider residual risks and decide whether it is worthwhile proceeding to detailed planning of risk response measures (B4).

B4 Respond to risks

B4.1   For each downside risk (other than those designated as negligible), decide what are the main options for avoiding, reducing, transferring or containing risks, by considering such actions as those listed below.

Reducing or eliminating risk: Risks can be reduced by re-designing, changing methods and/or materials, value engineering or changing contracting strategy.

Transferring risk: Risks can be re-assigned to the parties best able to control them or (if different) who will carry the risks at lowest cost – e.g. to government, contractors, concessionaires, operators, bankers, and other parties through contracts, financial agreements, franchise agreements, bonds and guarantees and other 'financial instruments'.

Insuring risk: Insurance is a particular form of third party risk transfer applicable to some categories of risk (see Appendix 5).

Avoiding risk: Risks can be avoided by changing the scope, design, and/or technology. In extreme cases, substituting for or abandoning the investment may be the only way a risk can be avoided.

Absorbing or pooling risk: Where two or more parties are each able to exercise partial control over the incidence and impact of risk, agreeing to share any adverse consequences can be an effective approach to mitigation.

Reducing uncertainty: Better information can be obtained on the probability distribution defining the risk and its potential impact, through feasibility studies or specific research. Consider other ways of managing uncertainty (see Appendix 1).

The effect of the risk mitigation measures will generally be to reduce downside volatility of the NPV and avoid worst-case scenarios, but at the likely cost of a reduced expected NPV (because of the cost of the mitigation measures).

Proceed similarly for upside risks, considering the options for widening the project's scope, increasing its revenue, increasing its life, improving the design, researching new technologies, improving the financial structure, involving partners, etc.

B4.2   Evaluate each risk response option, assessing:
- likely effect on risk, consequence and expected value
- feasibility and cost of implementing the option
- any 'secondary risks' resulting from the option
- further actions to respond to secondary risks
- overall impact of each option on cash flows.

Record options considered in the risk register. For this purpose, risk/response diagrams can be particularly useful.

B4.3   Choose the most effective option or options and record with reasons for the choice in the risk register. Increasing risk efficiency by simultaneously reducing expected cost and downside volatility is often possible and should be sought.

B4.4   Devise an action plan to implement each option.

B4.5   Group together common or related actions which respond to several risks simultaneously.

B4.6   Compile a 'risk response strategy', comprising all of the selected actions and the associated implementation plans, and include a 'risk response account' showing the costs and benefits of each response measure.

B4.7   Using the investment model, recalculate the NPV to take account of the effect of the selected response measures.

B4.8   Consider whether a better result can be obtained by excluding those response actions which have a high cost but limited beneficial effect on volatility. Some downside risks may need to be absorbed, unmitigated or only partially mitigated, because complete mitigation would be impracticable or too costly.

B4.9   Select risks which warrant an in-depth study of response possibilities. Generally these will fall into three groups

- those risks where there are apparently worthwhile response options but where confirmation is needed of their feasibility or cost
- those residual risks which are significant contributors to the downside volatility of NPV but for which no satisfactory mitigation measures have yet been identified
- those residual risks which are potentially significant contributors to the upside volatility of NPV and for which it is hoped that responses can be found which will increase the likelihood or impact of the events concerned.

B4.10   For each such risk, evaluate response options, repeating steps B4.1 to B4.7 above. Record the results from B4.1 to B4.10 in the risk register.

B4.11   Make a final decision on the set of responses which will be adopted. Record the extent to which risk efficiency has been achieved.

B5 Assess residual risks
Residual risks are those remaining after response measures have been taken.

B5.1   Assess the residual risks, allowing for the result of adopting the selected response measures, bearing in mind secondary risks and the cost of each measure.

B5.2   Sort residual risks into order of significance for each investment parameter.

B5.3   Using judgement, supported by Monte Carlo or other techniques, aggregate these risks for each parameter. Record the residual risks in the risk register.

B5.4   For each major activity affecting each parameter in each stage of the investment life-cycle, compile an estimate of the potential impact of residual unforeseen and unmeasured risks, based on experience and the complexity and uncertainties associated with the activity and parameter. Unmeasured risks are those foreseen risks which have not been measured or have been measured with a low degree of confidence. Consolidate these into contingency allowances for unforeseen and unmeasured risks relating to each parameter.

B5.5   Using the investment model, determine the overall impact on the investment (e.g. in terms of whole-life NPV) for each investment parameter, performing sensitivity analyses on the assumptions and estimates, and taking account of the contingency allowances in B5.4 above.

B5.6   In view of the expected value of the NPV, its volatility, the reliability of its measurements and

the potential consequences of the major risks, reconsider whether the investment is still worthwhile.

B5.7   Determine whether there is a version of the investment which would achieve (or nearly achieve) the same objectives with higher expected NPV and perhaps less volatility. If so, evaluate this alternative. Record the results in the risk response strategy.

B5.8   Obtain formal approval for proceeding with the project and for the risk response strategy, from the client and any other key stakeholders concerned (e.g. investors or lenders). See Section 5.15.

B6 Plan responses to residual risks
A 'risk response plan' is needed to minimise and contain the impact of remaining downside risks which cannot economically or practically be avoided or transferred, and to optimise any residual upside potential.

B6.1   For each residual risk or area of risk, assign responsibility for dealing with the risk to an appropriate 'risk custodian' and designate other parties responsible for specific actions within the risk response strategy.

B6.2   In consultation with the risk custodians and other designated parties, devise
- containment plans to minimise the downside risks and their impacts
- opportunity plans to increase the likelihood of favourable outcomes and to maximise their impacts if they occur
- contingency plans to deal with specific residual risks should they occur and for each define the 'trigger' events or circumstances in which the contingency plans will be implemented
- contingency budgets for the potential impact of the residual risks on each of the principal parameters of the investment.

B6.3   If it is envisaged that crises will be dealt with by a 'crisis committee', its members must be appointed in advance, with back-ups in case of non-availability, and full details of home and mobile telephone numbers, etc., communicated to all concerned.

B6.4   If the downside risk impacts, or costs of containing and responding to risks, are significantly higher than previously estimated, go back to B5.5.

B6.5   Assemble containment plans, opportunity plans, contingency plans and contingency budgets into a risk response plan.

B6.6   Obtain approval of client and other key stakeholders for risk response plan.

B7 Communicate strategy and plans

B7.1   At the end of the risk review, the risk process manager will critically assess the effectiveness of the review and the manner in which it was conducted, drawing lessons from the problems experienced and suggesting improvements for future risk reviews. This will be achieved, partly by reviewing the risk diary and other documents produced and partly by discussion with the client's representative and each of the other main participants.

B7.2   Compile a formal 'risk review report' outlining the main results of the review – including the main risks and their likely effects, and the overall riskiness of the investment – and the main lessons from B7.1.

B7.3   The risk review report should be considered in detail by client representatives responsible for the investment, who will need to review the continuance of the project and decide when the next risk review will take place and how it should be conducted.

B7.4   Prepare to communicate the relevant parts of the risk analyses, risk response strategy and risk response plans to those responsible for each remaining area of risk as described in steps B7.5 to B7.7. If the investment is to be aborted, go straight to Activity D (process close-down).

B7.5   Extract the relevant parts of the residual risk analysis, risk response strategy and risk response plan relating to risks assigned to each risk custodian and other parties involved in executing the strategies and responses.

B7.6   Supply the risk custodians and other parties with the appropriate extracts. Verify that these have been received and understood, and that those concerned are committed to undertaking the required action.

B7.7   Encourage all those involved to comment on or make suggestions about the residual risk analysis, risk response strategy or risk response plan, and give consideration to the implications of these. If necessary, make revisions to reflect the suggestions.

Activity C – Risk management
(See Chapter 7.)

The results of the risk review – notably, the risk analysis, risk response strategy and risk response plan – are then used to manage risks as part of the mainstream management of the investment. However, it is essential that the risk analysis, strategies and plans continue to be monitored and updated regularly as risk exposures change and risk events occur in between risk reviews. The organisation and processes for doing this must be embedded in the procedures for managing the investment as outlined below.

C1 Implement strategy and plans

C1.1   Ensure that, as far as possible, the risk response strategy and the risk response plan are integrated with mainstream investment, project and operating management processes, with single responsibilities and accountabilities assigned to named individuals for each action. In particular, ensure that there is effective follow-up to verify that appropriate plans and actions are implemented in a timely and satisfactory manner – e.g. contracts, financial agreements and insurance policies are concluded, 'trigger events' are observed, and payments made.

C1.2   Where special or exceptional actions are needed to deal with risks which cannot effectively be integrated within the mainstream management processes, ensure that clear responsibilities and accountabilities are assigned with reporting lines, or at least effective channels of communication, to the mainstream management.

C1.3   Ensure that any exceptional actions, required to contain or respond to risks outside the scope of main management activities, are co-ordinated with the main activities.

C1.4   Any significant changes or developments during the implementation of the risk response strategy and the risk response plan should be reported to the risk process manager.

C2 Control risks

C2.1   Verify that the risk response strategy and the risk response plan are adequately resourced and effectively implemented.

C2.2   Monitor progress against the risk response strategy and the risk response plan. Also monitor regularly all risks in the remaining stages of the investment life-cycle – not only the risks occurring in the present stage. Any significant changes in present or future risks should be reported and assessed immediately.

C2.3   Monitor risks regularly by studying events, situations or changes (sometimes called 'trends') which could potentially affect risks during the normal management and progress of the investment. These trends can be exposed through

- site visits
- progress reviews
- design meetings
- correspondence
- negotiations with contractors
- ground surveys
- market research exercises
- tests
- reports on other, similar investments.

These trends must be systematically identified, analysed and monitored on a regular basis by scrutinising reports, letters, and notes on visits, meetings and telephone conversations. Ideally, these should be considered at regular progress meetings (say weekly) involving key members of the investment management team. The trends can be usefully classified into one of three categories

- *potential (category P)*: to be assessed or observed more closely
- *expected (category E)*: mitigation or response measures to be taken
- *committed (category C)*: measures taken and then either treated as changes to the investment baseline plans, after evaluating and allowing for their impact, or provided for in the risk response strategy or risk response plan.

At each subsequent progress review meeting, the trends will be considered and may be eliminated or moved into another category. Generally, newly identified trends start in category P and then move first into category E and then into category C.

C2.4   As progress is made through the investment life-cycle, revise the residual risk analysis, risk response strategy and risk response plan, and release contingency budgets, as some risks materialise and other risk exposures change or disappear.

C2.5   When problems or significant changes in scope occur, revise relevant parts of the risk analysis, risk response strategy and/or risk response plan. If significant threats, changes, opportunities or developments occur, consider initiating an unscheduled risk review.

C2.6   Submit regular reports on progress, problems and changes to the client's representative and other key stakeholders (notably the project manager and operations manager).

C2.7   Regularly review whether the investment is still worthwhile.

C2.8   Decide whether (and when) a further risk review is required.

Activity D – Process close-down

(See Chapter 8.)

At the end of the investment life-cycle, or on prior termination of the project, a retrospective review will be made of the investment (in terms of its success and risk history) and of the contribution and effectiveness of the RAMP process itself as applied to the investment.

D1 Assess investment outturn

D1.1   The risk process manager, in conjunction with the client's representative, will first evaluate the performance of the investment, comparing its results with the original objectives.

D1.2   Using risk review reports and the risk diary, an assessment will be made of the upside and downside risks and impacts which occurred in comparison with those anticipated, highlighting risks which were not foreseen or grossly miscalculated.

D2 Review RAMP process

D2.1   The risk process manager will then critically assess the effectiveness of the RAMP process and the manner in which it was conducted for this investment, drawing lessons from the problems experienced and suggesting improvements for future investments. This will be done, partly by reviewing the risk diary, RAMP review reports and other documents produced, and partly by discussion with the client and each of the other main participants.

D2.2   The results of the review will be recorded in a 'RAMP close-down report', which can be easily referred to for future investments.

D2.3   Copies of the report will be circulated to all parties involved and then signed off by every party as an agreed record of events.

Appendix 10: Flowcharts of the RAMP process

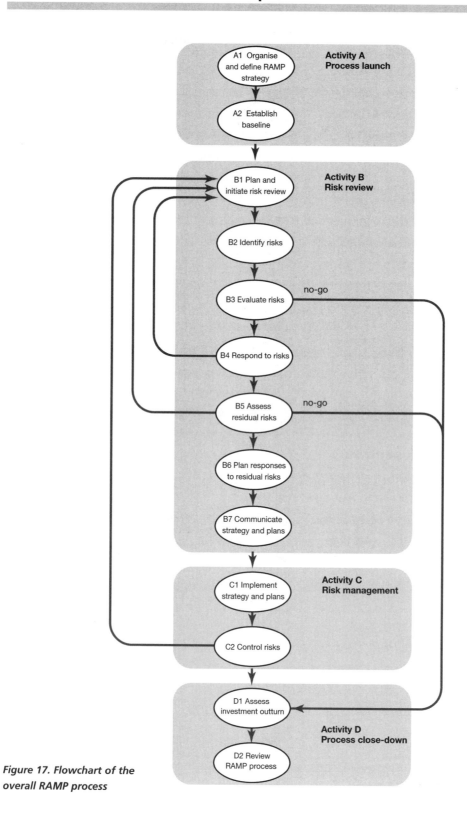

Figure 17. Flowchart of the overall RAMP process

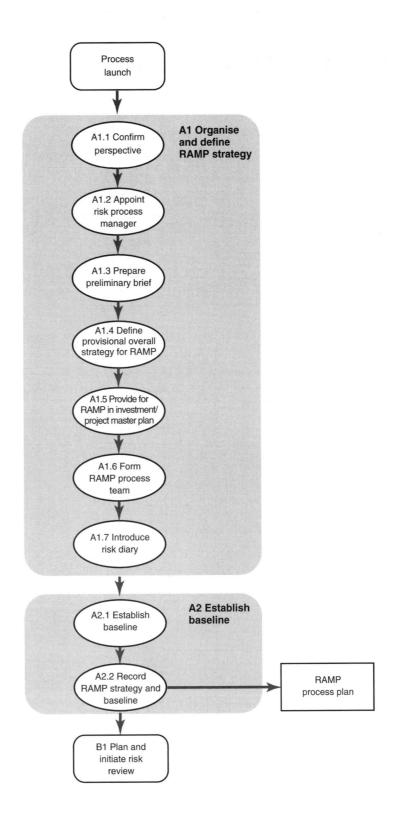

Figure 18. Activity A – Process launch

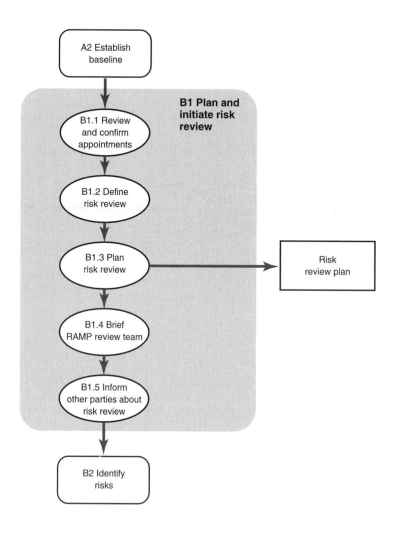

Figure 19. Activity B – Risk review: B1 plan and initiate risk review

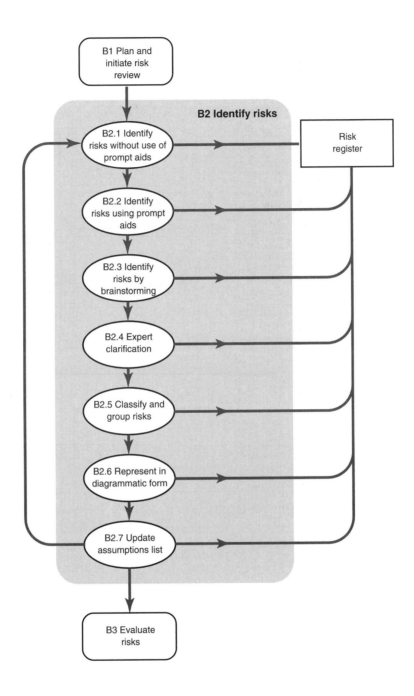

Figure 20. Activity B – Risk review: B2 identify risks

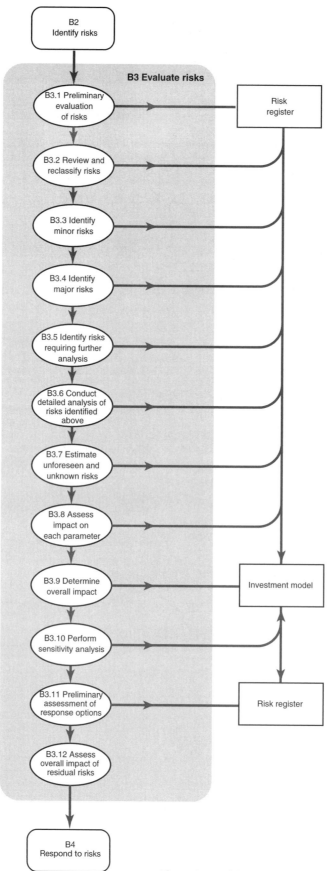

Figure 21. Activity B – Risk review: B3 evaluate risks

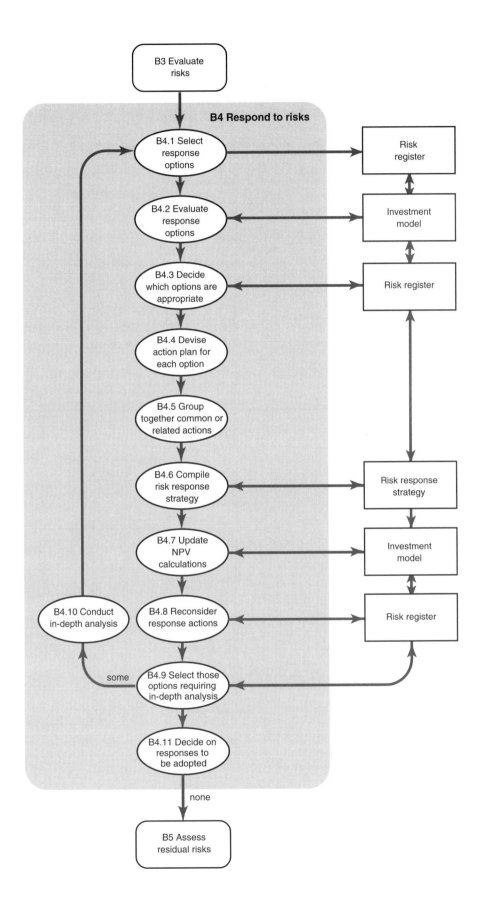

Figure 22. Activity B – Risk review: B4 respond to risks

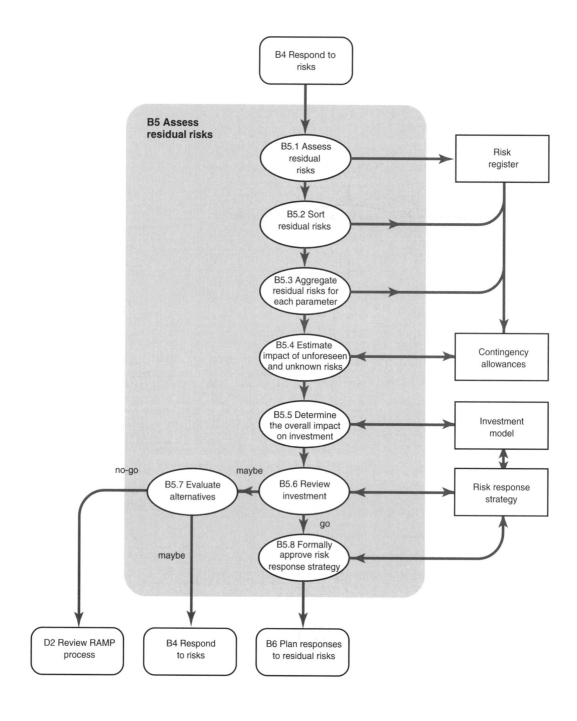

Figure 23. Activity B – Risk review: B5 assess residual risks

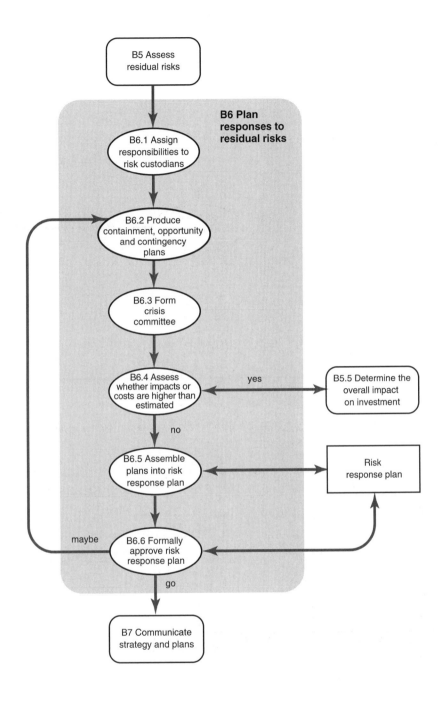

Figure 24. Activity B – Risk review: B6 plan responses to residual risks

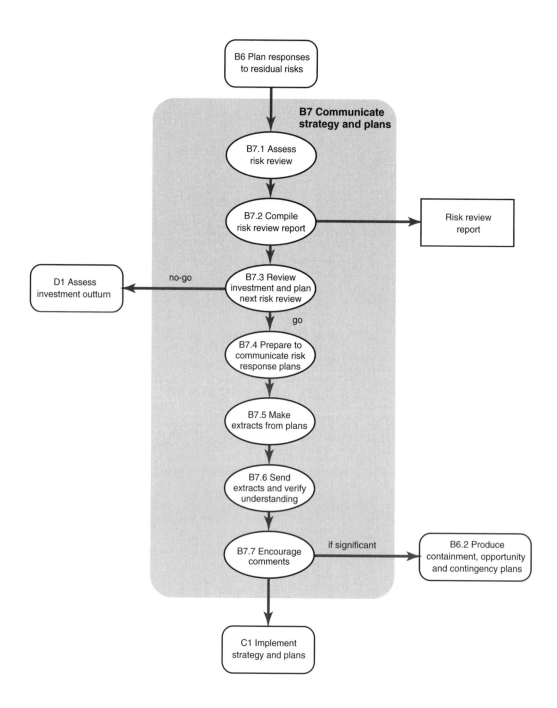

Figure 25. Activity B – Risk review: B7 communicate strategy and plans

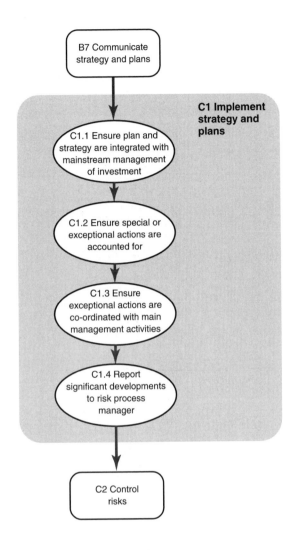

Figure 26. Activity C – Risk management: C1 implement strategy and plans

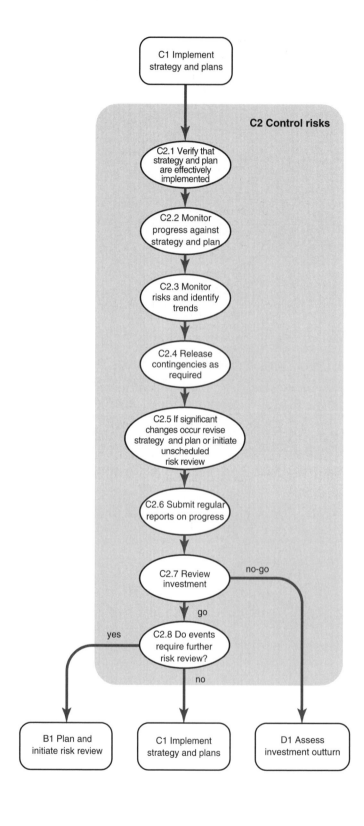

Figure 27. Activity C – Risk management: C2 control risks

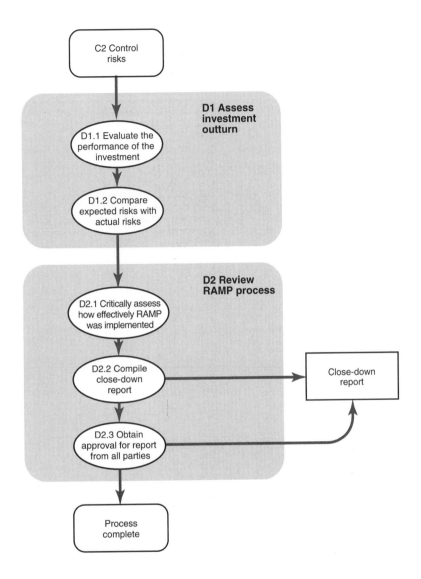

Figure 28. Activity D – Process close-down

Appendix 11: Key documents created in the RAMP process

Document	Purpose	Contents
RAMP process plan	To define strategy and basis for undertaking RAMP process over whole life of investment.	Investment brief and perspective, organisation and strategy for RAMP process, and baseline information.
Risk diary	To record significant events, issues and outcomes during RAMP process.	Significant events, problems, results, ideas for improvement and unforeseen risks arising.
Risk review plan	To describe the plan for carrying out a specific, individual risk review.	Risk process manager and review team. Purpose, scope and level of review. Action plan, resource requirements, budget and timetable.
Risk register	To record risk events and analyses (with separate sections for upside and downside risks).	Risk schedules: • Preliminary list of risks • Refined list of risks • Groups of risks • Risks where responses made • Residual risks. Individual risk analyses. Risk diagrams. Assumptions list.
Risk response strategy	To define the measures to be adopted to respond to risks.	Response measures, costs of responses and secondary risks.
Risk response plan	To define plans for containing or responding to residual risks.	Containment, opportunity and contingency plans and associated budgets. Responsibilities for action.
Investment model runs	To record the data and results of each run of the investment model.	Timing and purpose of run. Scenarios modelled. Parameter values. Resulting NPVs.
Risk review report	To summarise and report on results of risk review.	Main risks and potential effects. Summary of plans. Riskiness of investment. Lessons learnt. Significant changes arising from review.
Trend schedules	To identify, evaluate and act on new risks or changes in risk exposures and outcomes during the ongoing management of the investment.	Events, situations and changes (trends) which could affect risks, categorised into • potential • expected • committed.
RAMP close-down report	To report on overall performance of investment and effectiveness of RAMP process.	Comparison of investment plan (as authorised) against outturn result. Summary of risk history. Assessment of RAMP process as applied to investment. Suggested improvements to RAMP process for future use.

Table 30. Key documents created in the RAMP process

Appendix 12: Risks in major infrastructure projects

This Appendix describes some evidence which has emerged in recent years about the extent of the risks involved in major infrastructure projects and makes some recommendations for changes of approach in future.

Past experience – the evidence

Table 31 summarises some international past experience in one sector – urban rail, based on Allport, (2002). The broad conclusion is that, with a few notable exceptions, not only have the capital costs been underestimated (typically by 50% to 100%) but operating costs have been routinely underestimated (by a factor of two or three times), while revenues have been overestimated (typically by 100%). This has occurred in widely different environments and procurement regimes and there is no evidence of improvement. Major urban rail projects seem to be inherently more risky than most other transportation projects.

Where?	Parameter	Outturn compared with Forecast		Source
Europe/North America	Capital cost	Average more than 50% worse		Merewitz, 1973
USA	Capital cost	" "		Wachs, 1986
Developing Cities	Capital cost	Half the projects 50% to 500% worse Other half not as bad as this	))	Allport and Bamford, 1998
	Ridership	Half the projects 50% to 90% worse Other half not as bad as this	))	
USA	Capital cost Ridership	From 17% to 156% worse From 28% to 85% worse	))	Pickrell, 1990
Worldwide	Capital cost Ridership	From 15% better to 500% worse From 30% better to 90% worse	))	Skamris and Flyvbjerg, 1996
Worldwide (Private Sector)	Capital cost Ridership	No improvement over public sector " "	))	Allport and Bamford, 1998
UK, USA	Ridership	2 out of 13 'successful'		Mackett and Edwards, 1998
Asia (Private Sector)	Capital cost Ridership	No improvement over public sector " "	))	Halcrow, 2000
Worldwide	Capital cost	From 46% better to 200% worse (average 46% worse)	))	Skamris, 2000
	Ridership	From 96% worse to 1% better (average 51% worse)	))	
N. America,) UK)	Ridership	From 82% worse to 89% better (8 selected systems)	))	Babalik, 2000

Table 31. Record of financial success for major urban (metro/LRT) projects

For other types of public works project, a paper by Flyvbjerg et al. (2002) reports that, for capital cost, 'other types of project are at least as, if not more, prone to cost underestimation as are transportation infrastructure projects'.

Other evidence comes from the UK public sector, where a report by consultants Mott MacDonald (2002) showed that inadequate records were often retained relating to the original forecasts, but the remaining evidence pointed to significant and systematic under-forecasting of capital costs. Mott MacDonald studied 50 major projects, each costing over £40 million, and compared their planned and actual capital costs. They found that the average optimism bias (i.e. the percentage by which outturn capital cost exceeded the capital cost estimated at the outset) was as follows:

- Non-standard buildings   51%
- Standard buildings   24%
- Non-standard civil engineering 66%
- Standard civil engineering   44%

The works also typically took longer than expected.

Mott MacDonald found that the top six causes of optimism bias for capital cost were

- inadequacy of the business case (much the most important cause)
- environmental impact
- disputes and claims
- economic factors
- late contractor involvement in design
- complexity of contract structure.

However, Mott MacDonald also found that the optimism bias for PFI/PPP projects was much less than for traditionally procured projects, since for PFI/PPP projects the business case was more highly developed and more project risks were identified and mitigated.

A UK project not studied by Mott MacDonald, because it was then still under construction, was the new Scottish Parliament Building in Edinburgh. It was finished in 2004, about three years late, and a public enquiry was held to try and establish why the capital cost rose from £50 million to £431 million. The official report of the enquiry blamed Scotland's civil service, saying that the worst decision they made was to opt for construction management, which meant designing the building as it was being built, with the consequence that no proper budget could be set. This was compounded by a number of other mistakes and cultural failures. The management of the project was the subject of an audit report published in June 2004, which stated that 'the normal financial discipline of named individuals being accountable for controlling expenditure within limits specified in an approved budget was not present on this project. It seems that project management regarded the regular reports from the cost consultant on construction costs and on risk costs as setting a construction budget, when they were no more than forecasts'. The audit report also concluded that 'the approach to risk management was not fully consistent with good practice'. Twelve risk workshops took place between October 2000 and December 2002. These identified owners for specified risks but 'there was no monitoring or feedback on subsequent action'. No further workshops were held after December 2002 and 'there was thereafter no systematic basis for any action by project management to manage out risk, although the cost consultant continued to report its assessment of the cost of risk in accordance with its terms of engagement'. The audit report concluded that 'the form of contracting must always be chosen with care, with a sound appreciation of the risks and benefits of each of the procurement options… In complex public sector projects, the client should ensure that there is a single point of control and leadership for the project, with explicit authority and responsibility given to the person in charge.'

A recent guide published by the British Department for Transport produced estimates for the optimism bias which (they stated) should be introduced into the appraisal for the capital cost of transport infrastructure projects. The study, which also cited previous work by the consultants involved, was based on data from 172 road projects, 46 rail projects, and 34 bridges and tunnels. About three-quarters of the roads data related to the UK, while the data for the other projects were mainly non-UK and drawn from North America and Europe. The data suggested that the probabilities of a cost over-run of at least 1%, 20%, 50% or 100% were approximately as follows:

Probability of a cost over-run of:

	1% or more	20% or more	50% or more	100% or more
Roads	80%	40%	5%	–
Rail	83%	75%	33%	–
Bridges/tunnels	70%	50%	20%	5%

The study concluded that, for new projects, the extent to which the estimated capital cost (including standard contingency allowances) should be increased in the appraisal to allow for optimism bias depended on the willingness to accept the risk of a cost over-run, as follows:

Risk of a cost over-run

	50%	10%
Cost uplift		
Roads	15%	45%
Rail	40%	68%
Bridges/tunnels	23%	83%

The report usefully identified the following specific causes for cost escalation in transport projects

- changed requirements such as speed, road width, road type
- changed routing
- changed safety norms or building norms
- tighter environmental standards
- complex or extensive works – e.g. water or mountain
- unexpected archaeological finds
- under-estimated expropriation costs
- complex interfaces (urban environment, links to existing infrastructure)
- new or unproven technology
- construction costs
- calculation approach failing to allow for unplanned situations
- delays due to weather
- appraisal optimism by interested parties – for example a tendency for local authorities to give priority to presenting the virtues of a given project rather than its risks, because cost over-runs fall thinly on the population nationwide whereas the benefits of the project are local.

The report stated, however, that the inclusion of optimism bias may be unnecessary if advanced risk analysis is applied:

'It may be argued that uplifts should be adjusted downward as risk assessment and management improves over time and risks are thus mitigated. It is however our view that planners and forecasters should carry out such downward adjustment of uplifts only when warranted by firm empirical evidence. For 70 years, optimism bias has been high and constant for the types of transport projects considered above, with no indication of coming down. With practices of optimism as deep-rooted as this, hard evidence from post-audits would be required to convincingly argue the case that optimism bias is finally coming down. In general, only such a time when this evidence is available should uplifts be reduced accordingly. Having stated this general rule and precaution it must be observed that individual projects may exist where the claims to improved risk mitigation are so strong that downward adjustment of uplifts is warranted in order to avoid double counting. This may be the case if advanced risk analysis (e.g. risk identification work shop and statistical calculations of volume and cost risks for individual project components) has been applied and their results adequately reflected in the established budget.'

We regard a proper application of RAMP, including independent checking of the parameters and models, as 'advanced risk analysis' which should render the inclusion of optimism bias adjustments unnecessary. We believe that it is far better to rely on 'advanced risk analysis' than optimism bias, because the project will then be fully thought through at the outset. There will be a proper study of the mitigation of downside risk and the maximisation of upside potential, which is likely to increase the chance of a good outcome. Merely relying on the application of an 'optimism bias' uplift to the capital cost in the appraisal loses this advantage and also runs the risk of rejecting

Sector		Revenue source	Operating costs important?	Exogenous factors[1] important?	Gov't imp'n action important[2]?	Competition important?	Tariff issues[3]?	Scale of operating risk[4]
Transport	Roads-expressways	Tolls	No	Yes	Yes	Modest	Yes	3
	Rail-metro/LRT	Fares	Very	Yes	Very	Very	Yes	5
	High-speed rail	Fares	Very	Yes	Very	Very	Yes	5
	Airports	Landing fees, retail etc.	Yes	Very	Yes	Modest	Yes	2-3
	Ports	Tariffs	Modest	Very	Modest	Modest/Yes	Varies	2
Water	Supply[5] and Sanitation	User tariffs	Modest	Modest	No	No	Critical	2-3
Drainage/flood Control	Drainage	No	No[6]	No	No	No	Na	1
	Flood defence	No		No	No	No	Na	1
Power	Generating plants	Take-off contracts	Very (fuel)	Very	No	No	No	1-2
	Distribution	User tariffs	Modest	Yes	No	No	Yes	2-3
Health and Education	Hospitals and Schools	Varies[7]	Modest	No	No	No	Generally no	1
Public		No	No	No	No	No	Na	0

[1] macroeconomic, political, social, demographic factors
[2] e.g. in project identification, land acquisition and permissions, and integrating the project
[3] the ability to raise tariffs periodically
[4] on a scale from 0 = unimportant to 5 = very important. This qualitative assessment follows from the previous columns in the table
[5] includes water resources development
[6] can be significant for pumped drainage
[7] often no payment, availability payments under PFI, or direct payment

Table 32. Operating risk characteristics of infrastructure sectors

worthwhile projects for no sufficient reason, as well as providing the project manager with a large contingency budget that reduces the incentive for efficient construction of the capital assets. Another advantage of RAMP is the emphasis it places on risk management, at the appraisal stage and onwards, of the project's income and expenditure once the asset has been constructed and comes into operation; these 'operating risks' are often at least as important as the risks of capital cost over-run.

Operating risks

Unfortunately there seems to be very little hard data about the totality of the operating risks which have been experienced in the past for major projects. This is unfortunate, since the risk events occurring once a project has come into operation can have a crucial impact on the success or failure of the project, often to a greater extent than a variation in capital costs. Table 32 summarises the characteristics of the operating risks in typical infrastructure projects, based on the experience of practitioners. Major urban rail projects are at one extreme, success requiring many factors to go right and being readily undermined by a single poor decision or adverse occurrence. Such projects always have an uncertain operating surplus or deficit, are dependent upon strong government action and support, and are subject to strong competition and regulatory risk. One success story was London's Victoria Line, an underground railway built in the 1960s, where it was recognised at the outset that there was not a viable financial case for building the line but construction was justified on the basis of the quantified 'social benefits' which would accrue to the wider community once it came into operation, and the line has proved a very worthwhile addition to London's tube network (see Beesley and Foster, 1963). At the other extreme, social infrastructure projects of a standard nature

(such as hospitals and schools) tend to have less volatility in the eventual operating outcome compared with original expectations.

Forecasting operating risks

Operating risk occurs for many complex reasons and the scale and nature of the risks are not always appreciated at the outset. Too often the initial focus is dominantly on the huge task of completing the capital asset within budget and to time, and operating risks receive inadequate attention at that crucial point when the design can still be altered.

Practitioners' experience suggests that forecasts have often proved poor indicators of outturn operating results. The forecasting process is often complex and inherently uncertain, and as yet the uncertainties are rarely addressed with rigour. Some components are not always understood, for example rail operating costs. Forecasters may be motivated by a range of factors and they are not necessarily seeking to make a best estimate. Forecast revenues, in particular, are subject to very large margins of error. Operating forecasts are by their nature not verifiable until the project opens for business, and by that time corrective action may be able to have only a limited impact on commercial performance. The more flexible the design of the asset and the project as a whole can be, so as to permit changed modes of operation should this be necessary, the more likely it is that the initial operating performance will be satisfactory, even if circumstances have changed over the period (often of several years) since the design was decided upon. Moreover, a flexible design should be better able to adapt to changing and often unforeseeable circumstances over the period of many years during which it is hoped that the project will continue thereafter.

141

A need for change?

For social infrastructure of a standard nature (such as hospitals and schools) there may not need to be much change in existing practices relating to the forecasting and management of operating risks, though the use of a methodology such as RAMP should improve the chances of success significantly. In the case of other sectors, however, and notably in the transport sector, there may be a need for a radical change in approach, perhaps along the following lines:

- adapting the project development process and its staffing to serve the commercial needs of the project and its sponsors and investors;
- applying rigour in addressing risk and uncertainty, and drawing logical conclusions from this analysis (with the careful application of a methodology such as RAMP);
- not shrinking from taking account of 'social benefits, costs and risks' where necessary – i.e. benefits, costs and risks which will accrue to

sectors of the community other than the project sponsors and can be quantified in financial terms – though there may sometimes be a political need to turn some of the social benefits into financial benefits for the sponsor, for example by levying development charges on new buildings which will benefit from the project's improved infrastructure;

- providing a 'reality check' on forecasts produced by sophisticated models, by analysing the real-world experience of comparable projects and introducing independent checking of the parameters used;
- using independent audits and peer reviews by acknowledged experts, of the business case and the whole appraisal and risk management process, including the investment model, before irrevocable decisions are taken;
- building flexibility into the asset design and the project as a whole, even at extra cost, so as to allow the sponsor to respond flexibly to changing circumstances for many years into the future.

Select bibliography for Appendix 12

(**Note:** the main bibliography is on page 71)

Allport, R.J. (Halcrow). In which Cities and with which Policies can Metropolitan Railways provide the Backbone? *UITP Conference 'Metropolitan Railways'*, Shanghai, November 2002.

Allport, R.J. (Halcrow). World Bank Urban Transport Strategy - Mass Rapid Transit in Developing Countries, *UK Department for International Development/The World Bank*, July 2000.

Allport, R.J. and Bamford, T.J.G. (Halcrow Fox). Realising the Potential of MRT Systems in Developing Cities. *8th World Conference on Transport Research*, Antwerp, July 1998.

Allport, R.J. and Thomson, J.M. (Halcrow Fox). The Performance and Impact of Mass Rapid Transit in Developing Countries. *TRRL Research Report 278*, 1990.

Audit Scotland. Management of the Holyrood building project, June 2004.

Auditor General for Scotland. The new Scottish Parliament building – an examination of the management of the Holyrood project. September 2000.

Babalik, E. *Urban Rail Systems: A Planning Framework to Increase their Success*. PhD thesis, University of London, 2000.

Beesley, M. and Foster, C. Estimating the Social Benefits of constructing an Underground Railway in London. *Journal of the Royal Statistical Society, Series A (general)*, **126**, 46-78, 1963. Relates to the Victoria Line.

Flyvbjerg, B., Skamris Holm, M.K. and Buhl, S.L. Under-estimating Costs in Public Works Projects - Error or Lie? *American Planning Association Journal*, **68** (3), 279-295, 2002.

Flyvbjerg, B., Skamris Holm, M.K. and Buhl, S.L. How Common and How Large are Cost Overruns in Transport Infrastructure Projects? *Transport Review*, **23**, 1, 71-88, 2003.

Mackett, R. and Edwards, M. The Impact of Urban Public Transport Systems: Will the Expectations be Met? *Transportation Research*, **32A** (4), 231-245, 1998.

Merewitz, L. How do Urban Rapid Transit Projects compare in Cost Estimating Experience? *Proceedings, International Conference on Transport Research*, Brugge, 484-493, 1973.

Mott MacDonald. *Review of Large Public Procurement in the UK*. Report prepared for HM Treasury, July 2002.

Pickrell, D.H. *Urban Rail Transit Projects: Forecasts versus Actual Ridership and Costs*. Report DOT-T-91-04 UMTA US Department of Transportation, 1990.

Procedures for Dealing with Optimism Bias in Transport Planning - Guidance Document, British Department for Transport, prepared by B. Flyvbjerg in association with COWI, June 2004.

Skamris Holm, M.K. *Economic Appraisal of Large Scale Transport Infrastructure Investments*. PhD thesis, University of Aalborg, 2000.

Skamris Holm, M.K. and Flyvbjerg, B. Accuracy of Traffic Forecasts and Cost Estimates on Large Transportation Projects. *TRB Record No. 1518*, Washington D.C., 1996.

Wachs, M. Technique vs. Advocacy in Forecasting: a study of Rail Rapid Transit. *Urban Resources*, **4** (1), 23-30, 1986.

Index

Page numbers in italics refer to diagrams and flowcharts. The letter 'g' indicates a glossary reference.